A Manual for Introductory Astronomy

Revised 2012 Edition

Raymond J. Pfeiffer

CENGAGE
Learning·

Australia • Brazil • Japan • Korea • Mexico • Singapore • Spain • United Kingdom • United States

**A Manual for Introductory Astronomy:
Revised 2012 Edition**

Raymond J. Pfeiffer

Executive Editors:
Maureen Staudt
Michael Stranz

Senior Project Development Manager:
Linda deStefano

Marketing Specialist:
Courtney Sheldon

Senior Production/Manufacturing Manager:
Donna M. Brown

Production Editorial Manager:
Kim Fry

Sr. Rights Acquisition Account Manager:
Todd Osborne

For product information and technology assistance, contact us at
Cengage Learning Customer & Sales Support, 1-800-354-9706

For permission to use material from this text or product,
submit all requests online at **cengage.com/permissions**
Further permissions questions can be emailed to
permissionrequest@cengage.com

Compilation © 2012 Cengage Learning

ISBN-13: 978-1-285-13646-2

ISBN-10: 1-285-13646-2

Cengage Learning
5191 Natorp Boulevard
Mason, Ohio 45040
USA

Cengage Learning is a leading provider of customized learning solutions with office locations around the globe, including Singapore, the United Kingdom, Australia, Mexico, Brazil, and Japan. Locate your local office at:
international.cengage.com/region.
Cengage Learning products are represented in Canada by Nelson Education, Ltd.
For your lifelong learning solutions, visit **custom.cengage.com.**
Visit our corporate website at **cengage.com.**

Printed in the United States of America

A Manual for Introductory Astronomy

Table of Contents

*This exercise requires the use of **SKYLAB2,** astronomical software for IBM compatible machines, available from JCM Software, 600 Lawrenceville Road, Lawrenceville, New Jersey, 08648 or http://www.drdoz.com/jcm/index.htm.

Preface

With the recent "inflationary expansion" of our knowledge of the universe as a result of new technology, satellite telescopes, and space probes, authors have had to make some hard choices regarding what to include in an introductory textbook in astronomy. The result has been the gradual elimination of celestial sphere astronomy in favor of the new discoveries and the "new astrophysics." Perhaps this is because the new things are what excite most professional astronomers and authors, including myself. Unfortunately, it is becoming increasingly more difficult to find a thorough exposition of observational astronomy in the modern texts and celestial sphere astronomy is becoming a lost science and art.

I have found that many students are very much interested in learning about the changing panorama of the nighttime sky. Furthermore, most students at The College of New Jersey, who take our one semester, introductory astronomy course, do so in order to satisfy part of their liberal arts science requirements and are avoiding courses in chemistry and physics because of a weak background in science and mathematics. Therefore, our philosophy here at The College of New Jersey has been one in favor of having a considerable fraction of the course content directly related to what can be observed with the unaided eye. It is the latter that students will be able to experience and appreciate for the rest of their lives and not the physics that occurs in remote places of the universe. We have not eliminated the latter, merely relegated it to what we feel is its proper place at this academic level.

Hence, the need arose to develop this manual, which is used primarily for laboratory work. With the advent of computer labs on campuses and astronomical software that animates celestial motions, it has become possible to teach celestial sphere astronomy and do related laboratory work that was not possible before. I have had the good fortune to serve as a consultant in the development of such software, namely, *SKYLAB2*. In fact, this software is almost custom-tailored to our teaching needs. The result has been a software package designed for doing the exercises in this manual.

The material covered in this manual also reinforces what we teach in the classroom. For most exercises, there is an introductory section which presents most of the "missing matter" in today's astronomy texts. Therefore, this manual need not be used just for laboratory work. It can also be used as a textbook supplement or the exercises can be assigned for homework. Of course, full use of the manual requires the accompaniment of the software *SKYLAB2*. Amateur astronomers would also find this manual, along with *SKYLAB2,* helpful to teach themselves the main aspects of observational astronomy. This latest revision of the manual corrects many mistakes, typos, and language of previous versions

I would like to express my appreciation to JCM Software for permission to reproduce here many of the screen images that are available in *SKYLAB2*. I would also like to thank Paul Hiack for suggesting some of the exercises in this manual.

R. J. Pfeiffer
October 2010

Exercise 1.0

THE CELESTIAL EQUATORIAL COORDINATE SYSTEM

Equipment needed: A celestial globe showing positions of bright stars.

I. Introduction

There are several different ways of representing the appearance of the sky or describing the locations of objects we see in the sky.   One way is to imagine that every object in the sky is located on a very large and distant sphere called the **celestial sphere**. This imaginary sphere has its center at the center of the Earth. Since the radius of the Earth is very small compared to the radius of the celestial sphere, we can imagine that this sphere is also centered on any person or observer standing on the Earth's surface. Every celestial object (e.g., a star or planet) has a definite location in the sky with respect to some arbitrary reference point. Once defined, such a reference point can be used as the origin of a celestial coordinate system. There is an astronomically important point in the sky called the **vernal equinox**, which astronomers use as the origin of such a celestial coordinate system.   The meaning and significance of the vernal equinox will be discussed later.

In an analogous way, we represent the surface of the Earth by a globe or sphere. Locations on the geographic sphere are specified by the coordinates called **longitude** and **latitude**. The origin for this geographic coordinate system is the point where the Prime Meridian and the Geographic Equator intersect. This is a point located off the coast of west-central Africa. To specify a location on a sphere, the coordinates must be angles, since a sphere has a curved surface. Hence, longitude and latitude are angular distances from the origin described above.   Longitude is measured west or east from the origin (or prime meridian), and latitude is measured north or south from the origin (or geographic equator). If a ship happens to be located exactly at the geographic origin, we would say it has a longitude of 0 degrees (also written $0°$) and latitude of $0°$.

When one uses the celestial sphere to represent the sky, any measurements of position must also be angles. As on a geographic globe, two such angles are necessary to uniquely specify the location of any object on the celestial sphere.   The two angles or coordinates that astronomers use to specify position with respect to the vernal equinox are called **right ascension** and **declination**.

A peculiar thing about right ascension is that, though it is an angle, it is usually expressed in time units, that is, hours, minutes and seconds of time.   This is because there is a definite relationship between right ascension and something called **sidereal time** (sidereal time will be defined and studied in another, later exercise). An analogous relationship exists between longitude and time. A star located exactly at the vernal equinox would have a right ascension of 0 hours, 0 minutes (other ways of designating this are $0^h \ 00^m$ or 0:00) and a declination of 0 degrees, 0 arcminutes ($0° \ 00'$ or 0:00).

Note: Do not confuse minutes of time with arcminutes, they are not the same.   See part II.

Our objective now will be to use a model of the celestial sphere to locate objects using the coordinates right ascension (**RA** or α) and declination (**Dec** or δ). But first, we shall undertake a review of angular or arc measurement and how it is expressed and symbolized.

Exercise 1.0

II. Angular or Arc Measurement.

Any circle can be divided into any number of equal parts. For example, imagine dividing a circle into 4 equal parts. Any of these parts is called an **arc** and would be a certain fraction of the circumference of the circle; in this case, one fourth of a circumference. The ancient Babylonians found it convenient to divide a circle into 360 equal parts, which we call **degrees**. Thus,

One degree is 1/360th of a circle's circumference.

The Babylonians had an apparent fixation on multiples of 60, so they further divided each degree into 60 equal parts called arcminutes, or minutes of arc. That is,

1 arcminute (1') is 1/60th of a degree.

To allow for greater precision, they decided to divide each arcminute into 60 equal parts called arcseconds, or seconds of arc. Hence,

1 arcsecond is 1/60th of an arcminute or 1/3600th of a degree.

Such a system of measurement, based on the number 60, is called a **sexagesimal** system. We find a sexagesimal system far more difficult to use than a decimal system, but such a system did not daunt the Babylonians or the Egyptians and Greeks who also adopted this system. Unfortunately, it became so ingrained in early western civilization that it is still in common use for making angular measurements today. Thus we must learn to work with it. You should note that we also use a sexagesimal system for counting time. Often, we shall also want to express angular distance in decimal degrees. That is, 5^0 15' in the sexagesimal system is equivalent to 5.25 degrees in the decimal system.

PROBLEM 1: Write 15.67 degrees in sexagesimal notation on the answer sheet.

Remember that astronomers find it useful to express the celestial coordinate, right ascension, in time units. This is because the Earth rotates eastward on its axis, once every day. This makes the celestial sphere appear to turn at the same rate, but in the opposite direction, namely, westward. That is, if one faces south, stars would appear to move from the east towards the west, which would be from your left to your right and is referred to as the **apparent diurnal rotation of the celestial sphere.**

The rate of this motion is 15 degrees per hour. This number comes from the fact that Earth, or celestial sphere (you may assume one or the other rotates but not both), makes one complete turn through 360 degrees in 24 hours. This also means that the Earth rotates through an angle of 1 degree every four minutes of time. Since 1 degree contains 60', then the Earth turns 15' every 1m. This should point out the distinct difference between arcminutes and time minutes. One is an angle and the other is a time. **Never substitute one unit's abbreviation for the other, that is, never write 45' (forty-five arcminutes) when you mean 45m (forty-five minutes of time), or vice versa.**

PROBLEM 2: How much time does it take the Earth to rotate 65°?

First record your answer in hours and decimal parts thereof. Then convert the decimal part of an hour into minutes and record the hours and minutes also, like this: 7.33 hr. = 7^h 20^m.

III. Getting Acquainted with the Celestial Globe

Examine your celestial globe. The outer, transparent, plastic sphere represents the sky. Inside is a smaller sphere representing the Earth. A rod passes through the center of the Earth and extends outwards to touch the plastic sphere at two opposite points. This is the axis of rotation of the Earth or the Celestial sphere, depending on which you assume is rotating. The two points where the axis touches the celestial sphere are called the **north** and **south celestial poles, NCP** and **SCP**. Visually locate these two points on the globe. Also refer to the diagram below.

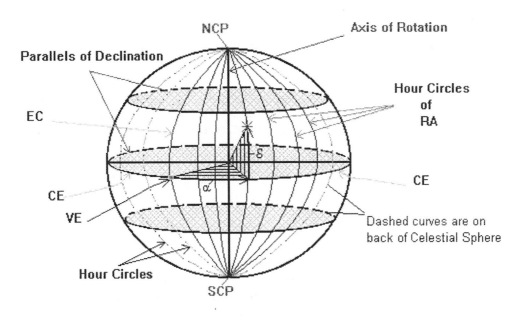

Midway between the poles is a great circle that divides the celestial sphere into two hemispheres. This circle is called the celestial equator (**CE**). Now find this circle on the globe and memorize the following definition.

Celestial Equator: The great circle on the celestial sphere, every point of which is exactly 90 degrees from the celestial poles.

There is a family of great circles that run from one celestial pole to the other and cross the celestial equator at a right angle. These are called hour circles of right ascension and they are analogous to meridians of longitude on the Earth. On the globe, hour circles of right ascension are drawn at regular intervals; these are considered to be fiducial circles, that is, they are circles indicating a precisely known value. Familiarize yourself with these circles on the globe now. Near the points where the hour circles cross the celestial equator, there should be a number that identifies the right ascension of that hour circle. Try to locate some of these.

Question 3: What is the interval, in hours, between the fiducial hour circles that are drawn and numbered on the globe? Write your answer on the answer sheet.

Remember that a point called the vernal equinox (**VE**) is the origin of our celestial coordinate system. This point is located on the celestial equator. Right ascension starts at the vernal equinox and increases eastward from there, all the way around the celestial sphere back to the vernal equinox again. That is, RA increases eastward from 0 to 24 hours. Hence, the number zero marks the hour circle passing through the vernal equinox. This hour circle is called the **equinoctial colure (EC)**. Now find this hour circle and the vernal equinox itself and make a mental note of where they are located on the globe.

Exercise 1.0

There is another family of circles, each member of which runs around the celestial sphere parallel to the celestial equator, anywhere between the latter and the celestial poles. These are called **parallels of declination** and are analogous to parallels of latitude on the Earth. All of these circles are smaller than the celestial equator and the closer one is to the celestial poles, the smaller it is. The celestial equator is itself a parallel of declination. See if you can locate these now. There should be a number written somewhere on each of these circles to identify what declination that circle represents.

Question 4: On the answer sheet, write the interval in degrees between the fiducial parallels of declination that are drawn on the globe.

Declination is an angle measured north or south from the celestial equator. This angle can be imagined as an arc drawn on the globe starting at the celestial equator and extending along an hour circle to the parallel of declination passing through the object we are trying to locate. Note and memorize the following:

Right ascension (α) is the angular distance measured eastward around the sky from the vernal equinox.

Declination (δ) is the angular distance measured north (+) or south (-) from the celestial equator.

All objects located on the same parallel of declination have the same declination but different right ascensions. Similarly, all objects located on the same hour circle have the same right ascension but different declinations.

IV. Locating Objects on the Celestial Globe by Interpolation

In order to locate an object on the celestial sphere, remember the following rule:

Through any object on the celestial sphere, one can draw a definite hour circle of right ascension and a definite parallel of declination.

That is, the hour circles and declination parallels that are already drawn on the globe are referred to as **fiducial** ones, but they are not the only ones that could be drawn. Hence, if the parallel of declination passing through an object is not exactly one of the fiducial values, you will need to employ a technique called **interpolation** to determine the value of that object's declination, δ. For example, if an object has a declination of 17° 30', and the fiducial parallels of declination are drawn every 10° apart on some hypothetical globe (not necessarily your globe), you will need to know what fraction of the distance between the 10th and 20th parallels corresponds to this declination. The fractional distance from the 10th parallel towards the 20th parallel would be (17.50-10.00)/(20.0-10.0) or 7.50/10.00=0.75, that is, 3/4ths the distance. Notice that we have converted the sexagesimal value of 17° 30' to its decimal equivalent, 17.50 degrees, with 2 decimal place precision, for convenience in using a calculator. Now we use a flexible ruler and measure the distance between the 10th parallel and the 20th parallel. Suppose this number is 2.85cm. (the value on your globe is not this value). Therefore, the object is located a distance of 2.85cm x 0.75=2.14cm from the 10th parallel towards the 20th parallel. We now use our ruler to locate the position of the parallel of declination that passes through our object.

Similarly, if a star has RA=7^h 20^m, its hour circle is on third of the distance from the 7th hour circle to the 8th hour circle. This is because 20^m is 1/3rd (or 0.33) of an hour. We now proceed as for declination and use a flexible ruler to measure the distance between hour circles. Unlike for declination, our result will depend on what declination circle we make this measurement. Let us say we choose to make this measurement along the celestial equator and that the result is 4.27cm. Then the hour circle passing through our object is located 4.27cm x 0.33 = 1.41cm from the 7th hour circle towards the 8th hour circle, and we measure this distance along the celestial equator. You should now know what to do if hour circles are not drawn on the globe for every hour.

V. Assignment

Part 1

Now locate and identify the objects, which have their coordinates listed on the answer sheet, and the constellations in which they are located. Stars are identified by lower case letters, whereas constellations are identified by upper case letters. Be careful not to confuse the two. With a few exceptions, stars that are in the same constellation are connected by lines. Note this.

Objects appearing like asterisks and identified by an upper case "M" followed by a number, such as, **M52**, are objects in Messier's Catalogue and are usually star clusters, nebulae, or galaxies. If one of the objects you identify is a Messier object, it is not necessary for you to know which kind of object it is, just write your answer to be the Messier designation, such as, **M101**. Don't forget, Messier objects, like stars, are located in a constellation.

Warning, the term "ECLIPTIC", the months of the year, and "PE" are also engraved on the globe and are not constellations and cannot be answers.

Part 2

Search over the surface of the globe to find 3 other Messier objects. This is most readily done by visually scanning north to south within 1 hour bands of right ascension (RA) at a time. By visual interpolation, determine the RA and Dec. coordinates for these objects and record the results on the answer sheet using the proper format (RA=7^h 20^m ; Dec. = -17° 30'). Do not use colons. Be as precise as you can. Do not look up the exact coordinates on line or in a reference, since those values will be somewhat different than what you will read from the celestial globe.

Now go online to http://www.seds.org/messier/data2.html. Then click on the link "messier index." Go down the list and identify the Messier objects as either a nebula, a galaxy, an open cluster, or a globular cluster, and fill in the blank on the answer page.

ANSWER SHEET
EQUATORIAL COORDINATES ON A GLOBE

II. Angular Measurement

    1. Sexagesimal equivalent of 15.67°: _____

    2. Time for rotation of 65°: _____

III. Getting Acquainted with the Celestial Globe

    3. Spacing of reference hour circles drawn on the globe in hours: _____

    4. Spacing of reference declination parallels drawn on the globe in degrees: _____

V. Part 1: Identification of Objects on Celestial Globe

	RA	DEC	Object	Constellation
1.	4:36	+16:29	_____	_____
2.	5:14	-08:13	_____	_____
3.	5:15	+46:15	_____	_____
4.	5:33	-05:20	_____	_____
5.	6:45	-16:42	_____	_____
6.	7:39	+05:15	_____	_____
7.	7:42	+28:00	_____	_____
8.	14:16	+19:13	_____	_____
9.	16:27	-26:15	_____	_____
10.	16:42	+36:28	_____	_____
11.	18:35	+38:44	_____	_____
12.	19:50	+08:50	_____	_____

V. Part 2: The Messier Catalog

For RA, use superscripts h for hours and m for minutes, not colons. For declination use degree symbols for superscripts and the symbol, ', for arcminutes. Do not use colons.

	RA	Dec.	Object	Constellation	Type of Object
1.	_____	_____	_____	_____	_____
2.	_____	_____	_____	_____	_____
3.	_____	_____	_____	_____	_____

Exercise 2.0

RECTANGULAR STAR-CHARTS

I. Introduction

In Exercise 1.0, we studied how the sky is represented by a sphere and how objects are located on the sphere using the astronomical coordinates called right ascension (RA) and declination (Dec). Another way to represent the sky is by means of a flat, 2-dimensional chart or map. In geography, this is analogous to having a flat map of the Earth, or a simple road map. There are several ways to represent a curved sphere by a flat map. The one that we shall use in this exercise is referred to as a **rectangular projection**.

With a flat map of the Earth, we can continue to represent locations by using the coordinates of longitude and latitude. Similarly, to locate a star on a flat chart of the sky, we still need to specify the two coordinates, right ascension and declination. However, now we can also measure distances on the chart in linear units such as centimeters or inches. The arithmetical relation between the angular units and the linear units is called the **Chart-Scale**. For example, 1 cm = 4 degrees. The reciprocal or inverse of this chart scale is 1 degree = 0.25cm. Knowing the scale of a chart enables one to plot positions very precisely, using a ruler rather than a protractor. Determining the chart-scale for a star-chart and using this to identify certain stars on the chart is our objective in this exercise.

II. Determining a Chart-Scale

A star-chart may be found on a page at the end of this exercise. This chart is a rectangular projection of the celestial sphere. Remember the following precept:

Any linear distance on a rectangular chart corresponds to an angle on the curved surface of the celestial sphere.

Because a sphere can not be cut open and laid out flat, a rectangular projection chart introduces some distortion of the curved surface that it represents. The greater the area of the sphere it tries to represent, the more distortion there is near the top and bottom of the chart. Since a flat map or chart is such a great convenience, we learn to live with this distortion.

Now look at the star-chart at the end of this exercise. This chart has a grid of vertical and horizontal lines drawn on it. Remember that these lines represent circles on the celestial sphere.

The vertical lines represent fiducial hour circles of right ascension and the horizontal lines represent fiducial parallels of declination.

These are known as fiducial lines, because we can trust them to indicate definite celestial locations. These fiducial lines will enable you to determine the scale of the chart. To do this, we shall need to measure the distance between these lines with a centimeter ruler.

The centimeter ruler can be read to a definite tenth of a centimeter and a guess can be made of the **hundredth of a centimeter** by interpolation. This is how you should always read the ruler in this course. Now proceed as follows:

Exercise 2.0

1. Take your centimeter ruler and measure the distance between the left margin of the chart and the right margin, somewhere in the middle of the chart. Record your answer at the bottom of the answer sheet on the line for the RA chart scale. Also write down the corresponding number of hours of RA to which this distance corresponds, like this: 24^h = 11.56 cm.

2. Now divide the distance in centimeters by the corresponding amount of hours. This yields the chart scale in centimeters per hour (cm/hr). Record your result on the appropriate line. Taking the inverse of this number, or dividing the hours by the distance, yields the chart scale in hours per centimeter (hr/cm). We shall not need this value.

3. Now follow a similar procedure as above and make a measurement of the distance between the top margin of the chart and the bottom margin. Record your measurement on the answer sheet on the line for the declination chart scale along with the corresponding number of degrees of declination to which this measurement refers.

4. Divide the number of centimeters by the correspond number of degrees to get the declination chart scale in cm/deg. Record the result on the answer sheet.

III. Locating and Identifying Stars

Once you have the two chart scales, you can proceed to identify the exact places on the large chart where the stars listed in the table below are located. The table lists the names (if there is one), the Bayer designation, and equatorial coordinates for some of the brightest stars in the sky. The Bayer designation consists of a lower case Greek letter and the 3 letter abbreviation of the constellation in which the star is located.

Use the tabulated values of right ascension and declination for each of these stars to locate them on the star-chart. Proceed as follows:

1. First convert the sexagesimal coordinates for both RA and Dec. to decimal values, before you try to multiply by the appropriate chart scale. Write these decimal values in the blank spaces in the columns of the table that have the headers **Deciα** and **Deciδ**.

2. Multiply the **Deciα** and **Deciδ** values by the appropriate chart scale to find the distance of the star in centimeters from either the equinoctial colure for RA, or the celestial equator for Dec.

3. Now use your ruler and measure the RA distance in cm from the right margin of the chart towards the left. Do this at two widely spaced positions, one near the top of the chart and the other near the bottom and make a mark to indicate these positions.

4. Now connect these two marks with a faint, straight line. This line will be the star's hour circle of RA.

5. Now repeat for the declination, measuring upwards from the celestial equator if the declination is positive and downwards if negative. Again, do this at two widely spaced positions, one on the left side of the chart and the other on the right.

6. Connect these two points with a straight line. This line is the star's parallel of declination.

7. Where these two lines intersect should be the exact location of the star.

8. Identify these stars by using a fine-point pencil and carefully print the Bayer designation (not the proper name) near the star image on the star-chart. Then draw a small arrow to connect the abbreviation with the star-image. **Make sure the arrowhead actually touches the star image unambiguously.** Or, draw a small circle around the star and draw the arrow touching that circle, but make sure the circle that you draw encloses only one star.

Below is a schematic diagram that attempts to illustrate how the stars are to be identified. Make sure your chart looks exactly the same.

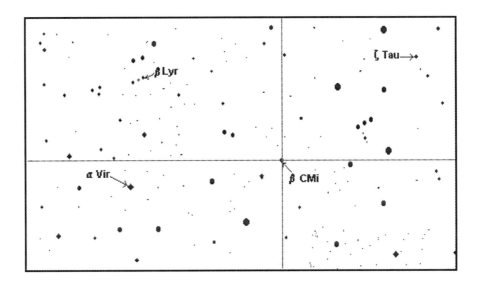

The above diagram is meant to show how you are to identify the stars on your star chart. It is not a real star-chart. The hour circle of RA and parallel of Dec. are drawn for a hypothetical star identified as β CMi.

ANSWER SHEET FOR STAR CHART EXERCISE

Table of Stellar Coordinates

Star Name	Abbrev.	R. A.	Dec.	Deciα	Deciδ	RA(cm)	Dec(cm)
Schedar	α Cas	0ʰ 41ᵐ	+56° 35'	_____	_____	_____	_____
Acamar	θ Eri	2 59	-40 16	_____	_____	_____	_____
Bellatrix	γ Ori	5 26	+ 6 21	_____	_____	_____	_____
Canopus	α Car	6 23	-52 40	_____	_____	_____	_____
Wasat	δ Gem	7 21	+21 58	_____	_____	_____	_____
Algieba	γ Leo	10 20	+19 48	_____	_____	_____	_____
Algorab	δ Cor	12 30	-16 14	_____	_____	_____	_____
Mufrid	η Boo	13ʰ 55ᵐ	+18° 02'	_____	_____	_____	_____
Izar	ε Boo	14 43	+27 17	_____	_____	_____	_____
	ε Sco	16 51	-34° 18'	_____	_____	_____	_____
Aldhibah	ζ Dra	17 09	+65 42	_____	_____	_____	_____
	δ Cyg	19 44	+45 00	_____	_____	_____	_____
Dabih	β Cap	20 21	-14 45	_____	_____	_____	_____
	ε Peg	21 45	+9 55	_____	_____	_____	_____
Fomalhaut	α PsA	22ʰ 55ᵐ	-28° 53'	_____	_____	_____	_____

Table of Data for Chart Scale

Record data for determining the chart scales for RA and Dec below:

Measurements and calculation of RA chart scale:

Measured distance in cm (to hundredth place) _____ = _____ hours of RA.

RA chart scale (divide cm by hours) to 4 significant figures _____ cm/hr.

Measurements and calculation of Dec. chart scale:

Measured distance in cm (to hundredth place) _____ = _____ degrees of Dec.

Dec. chart scale (divide cm by degrees) to 4 significant figures _____ cm/deg.

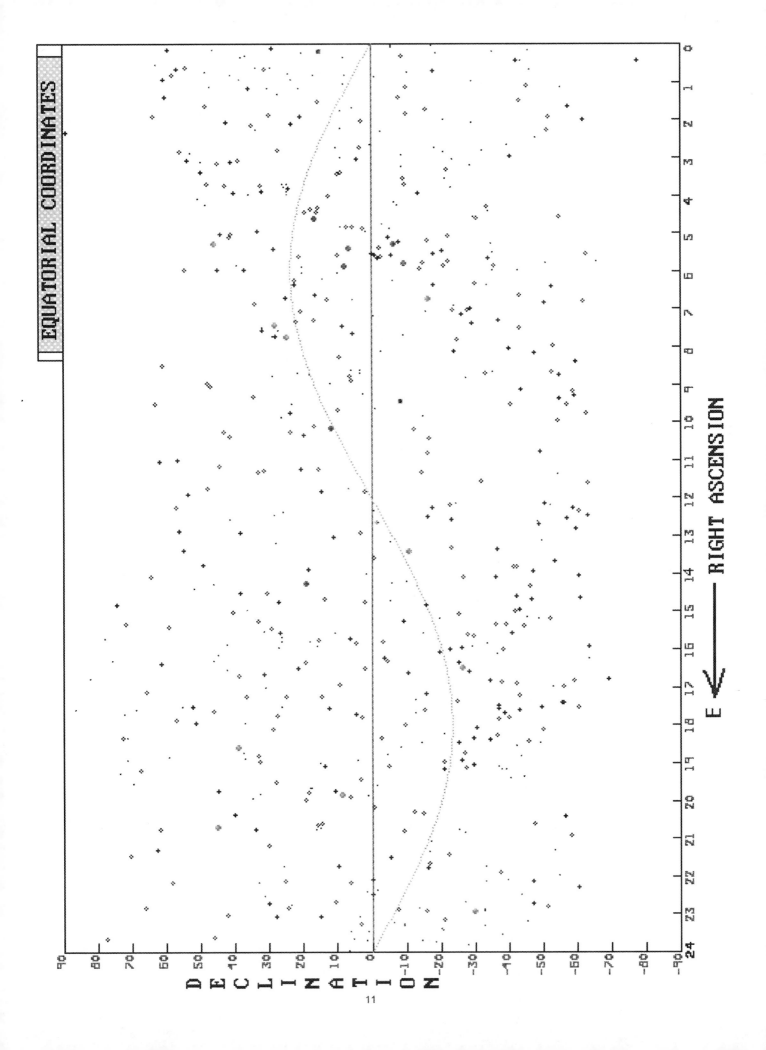

EQUATORIAL COORDINATES

RIGHT ASCENSION

E

DECLINATION

11

Exercise 3.0

LOCATING CONSTELLATIONS IN THE EQUATORIAL COORDINATE SYSTEM

I. Introduction

The purpose of this exercise is to acquaint you with some of the traditionally recognized patterns of stars visible to the unaided eye. These patterns, called constellations, were developed more than 3000 years ago by the ancient civilizations that lived in the eastern Mediterranean Region. In this exercise, you are going to identify some of these constellations on the star chart below by using the SKYLAB2 software.

II. Procedures

Logon to SKYLAB2 and from the Main Menu select "Star Atlas". A rectangular star chart like the one given to you at the end of this exercise will come up on the screen. Several hundred of the brightest stars visible to the unaided eye are represented on this chart. The brightness of a star (which astronomers call "magnitude") is indicated by the number of little illuminated dots that make up the image for a given star; the more bright dots, the brighter the star. Of course, on the printout, the bright dots become black dots. Your objective now is to find out which stars belong to the following constellations:

Andromenda	Aquila	Aquarius	Aries
Auriga	Bootes	Capricornus	Cassiopeia
Canis Major	Cancer	Cetus	Corona Borealis
Cygnus	Gemini	Hercules	Leo
Libra	Lyra	Ophiuchus	Orion
Pegasus	Perseus	Pisces	Scorpius
Sagittarius	Taurus	Ursa Major	Virgo

When the stars belonging to each of these constellations have been identified, you are to draw an encompassing boundary around all of them in that constellation and then print the three letter abbreviation for that constellation, inside the boundary. The three letter abbreviation can be found in the table of constellations selected as an option under "Star Atlas." An example already exists for the constellation Corvus on the star chart below. Examine this to see what it is that you are to do. In fact, you may want to verify the boundary for Corvus.

To begin from where you are now, type "O" for the options window. Now cursor down to highlight "Constellations" and press the Enter key. This should bring up the table of constellations and their abbreviations. Cursor to highlight the constellation you want to identify and then press Enter. The star chart will now be redrawn, but showing only the stars for the constellation you highlighted in the table. Do not press the escape key to remove the options window, unless it interferes with the constellation. This will make it easier to go from one constellation to the next.

Now take the star chart below and identify the stars on it that belong to the constellation by comparison with the constellation chart on the monitor screen. You can be aided by making use of the right ascension and declination coordinates. As you match up the stars on the screen with the stars on your chart, you can begin to draw the perimeter around the constellation. The boundary of one constellation may not cross the boundary of another. However, two constellations may share, in part, a common boundary, just as two countries may have a common border in part.

Once the perimeter is completed so that it encompasses all the stars in the constellation, you can print the abbreviation inside the boundary. Now you are ready to go to the next constellation. If the options window is still on the screen and "Constellations" is still highlighted, you need only press the Enter key and the table of constellations will come back. Now cursor to the next constellation and proceed as above. If you pressed the Escape key to remove the options window, it will now be necessary to type "O" again and proceed as before.

Warning: Some constellations near the edges of the chart continue, or wrap around, to the other edge of the chart. Be sure not to miss these stars.

Once you have completed this exercise, it will serve later to aid you in actually locating these constellations in the sky. However, the constellations that are visible in the evening sky depend on the season and time you observe. These matters will be discussed in later exercises.

Check with your instructor on how this exercise is to be graded. As always, your grade will depend on how carefully and accurately you have done the assignment.

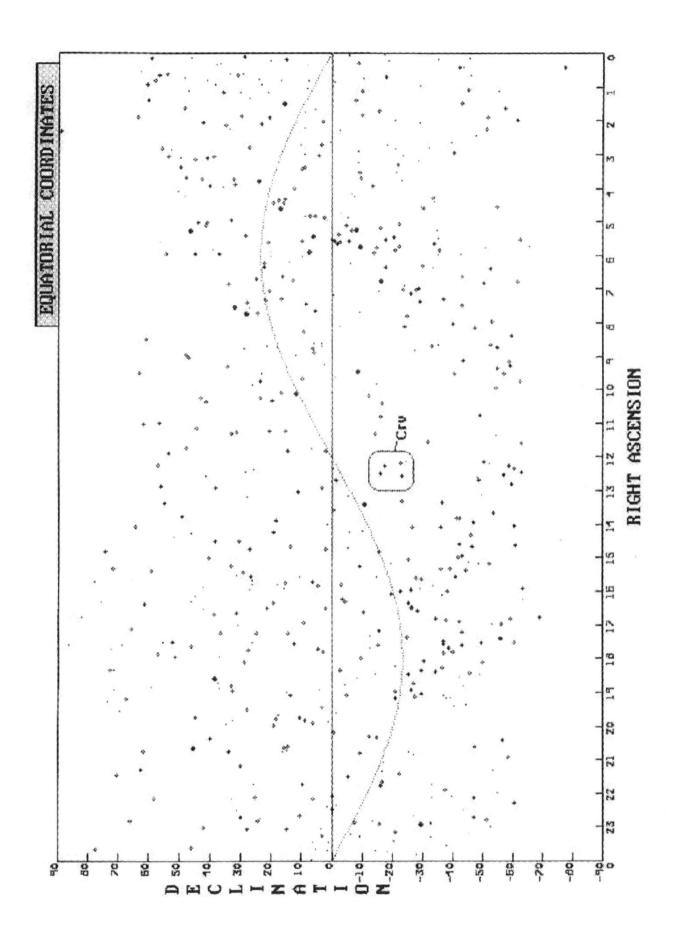

EQUATORIAL COORDINATES

RIGHT ASCENSION

DECLINATION

Crv

15

Exercise 4.0

OBSERVATION OF THE SKY WITH THE UNAIDED EYE

I. Introduction

The purpose of this exercise is to have you become a familiar with the night sky. In this exercise you will use star charts to help you locate some constellations and other objects in the sky visible to the unaided eye. You will use SKYLAB2 to make a chart of the location of objects in the sky for the day, time, year, and location of your choice. It is assumed you are familiar with both the celestial equatorial system of coordinates and the horizon system. You will also determine where the cardinal points of the compass are located on the horizon for the site where you will make your observations. This will enable you to visualize how your local celestial meridian (LCM) arcs across the sky.

II. Procedure - Inside

1. Logon to SKYLAB2 and go to the program Star Atlas.

2. Use the Coordinates menu to select the Horizon System.

3. Use the Time/Date menu to set the time, date and year to correspond to when you will be doing your observations. (Do not forget to use a 24-hour clock.)

    The program is set for the latitude, longitude and zonetime of TCNJ. These settings should be adequate for most nearby locations. However, if you know the coordinates of the location where you will be observing, enter them using the Location menu.

4. Use the Options menu to select Grid and again to set the Cutoff to Magnitude 4. Also add Constellation Abbreviations.

5. Use the Zoom menu to zoom in by a factor of 2X

6. Use the Pan menu to pan up by 45 units. The sky appears as you would see it if facing south, i.e., the sky is seen from the East point to the South point to the West point.

7. Use the Pan menu to pan left by 6 units. The sky appears as you would see it if you were facing east, i.e., the sky is seen from the North point to the East point to the South point.

8. Get a printout of this chart.

9. Use the Pan menu to pan right by 12 units. The sky appears as you would see it if you were facing west, i.e., the sky is seen from the South point to the West point to the North point.

10. Get a printout of this chart.

11. Under options change the Cutoff Magnitude to 5 or 6 for a more realistic view of the sky.

12. Look at the Symbols menu to review the symbols used for the Sun, Moon, and Planets.

The charts you have obtained are specific for the date and time you chose. Remember that the sky turns at the rate of 15° per hour around the pole and parallel to the equator (Diurnal Motion). Remember also that stars move 1 degree per day westward with respect to their position the previous day (the Westward March of the Constellations). *These motions are described in the Celestial Equator Coordinate System and are not directly transferable to the Horizon System.* However, your charts should be usable for several days before or after the date you chose if you observe at the same time or even for an hour or so before or after the time you chose provided you allow for the diurnal motion.

(You may wish to open the SKYLAB2 Program "Skymation", set the Coordinates to the Horizon System, Zoom out by a factor of 2X and allow the motion to run to observe how the Altitude and Azimuth of the stars change with diurnal motion.)

III. Procedure – Outside

1. Determine the location of the **Cardinal Points of the Compass** for the location of your observation.
    a. Use the "pointer stars" of the "Big Dipper" (Ursa Major) to find **Polaris**. It is located about 5 times the distance between these stars along a line through them. (See Fig.1)

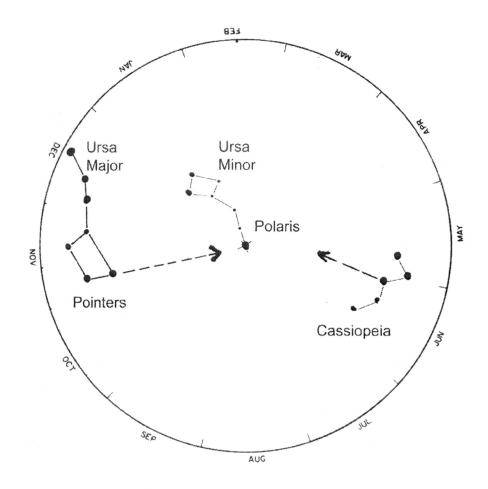

Fig. 1. A view of the circumpolar region of the celestial sphere with the north celestial pole at the center of the circle.

18

Exercise 4.0

  b. If the "Big Dipper" is hard to see, you can use Cassiopeia to locate Polaris. Cassiopeia can be viewed as a "W" and the "Little Dipper" (Ursa Minor) with Polaris at the end of the handle directly above it. Since some of the stars of the "Little Dipper" are not very bright, you may only be able to see Polaris, β, and γ. (See Fig. 1) The chart will show the positions of these constellations in the sky if it is held so that the month of observation is at the bottom.

  c. Draw an imaginary line from the point directly over your head (the Zenith) through Polaris down to the Horizon. This is the **North point**. Find an object (house, tree, etc.) that marks this point. Note it on the line below.

  d. Face the North point and locate an object 90ᵒ to your right on the Horizon. This is the **East point**. Note it below.

  e. In the opposite direction from the East point is the **West point**. Locate an object there and note it below.

  f. Opposite the North point on the Horizon is the **South point**. Locate an object there and note it below.

  g. The imaginary half circle across the sky from the North point to the South point is your **Local Celestial Meridian (LCM).**

    North point object _____

    East point object _____

    West point object _____

    South point object _____

2. To estimate angles on the Celestial Sphere we can make use of the following:

  a. The angular size of the Sun or the Moon is about ½ °.

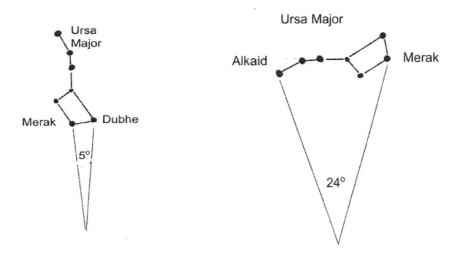

Fig. 2. Angles represented for the Big Dipper in Ursa Major.

  b. The separation of the Pointer Stars in the "Big Dipper" is about 5° and the distance from the end of the "handle" of the "Dipper" to the "bowl" is about 24°. (See Fig. 2)

c. The Altitude of Polaris (the angular distance above the Horizon) is equal to your latitude, about 40° for TCNJ.

d. You can use your "fist" held with your arm extended to as a rough gauge of angles. At arms length:
    i. A thumbnail has an angular size of about 1°.
    ii. The first 2 knuckles are about 2° apart.
    iii. The entire fist spans about 10°.
    iv. With the hand spread out as far as possible, the distance from the thumb tip to the end of the little finger is about 20°.

e. *Use the information above to determine how your "fist" conforms to these numbers.*

f. Use this method to determine the angles requested in the rest of the exercise.

3. Observe the motions of the stars.

a. Trace out the location of the Celestial Equator in the sky. It crosses the Horizon at the East point, the Local Celestial Meridian (See step 1. g. above) at an Altitude, i.e., an angular distance above the Horizon equal to the compliment of your latitude. (For TCNJ this is at 50°, i.e., 90° - 40°.)

b. At the beginning of your observation estimate as accurately as possible the position of (a) Polaris, (b) a star close to the East point of the Horizon, and (c) a star close to the West point of the horizon. Enter the data in the table below.

c. At the end of your observing session again estimate the altitude and azimuth of these same stars. Enter the data in the table. How have they changed?

Object	Original Altitude	Original Azimuth	Final Altitude	Final Azimuth
Polaris				
East point Star				
West point Star				

d. What can you conclude about the motions?

e. Do the East and West point stars seem to move parallel to the Horizon or the Celestial Equator?

4. The brightness of stars is measured with a system first developed by the Greek Hipparchus. The brightest stars are called "first magnitude" (V = 1), the next brightest stars are called "second magnitude" (V = 2), and so on. The system has been refined and standardized but is still in use. We will use the stars of the "Little Dipper" (Ursa Minor) to estimate the limiting magnitude, i.e., the faintest stars that can be seen with the unaided eye.

a. Locate the "Little Dipper" in the sky and on the diagram below check off each of the stars that you can see.

Exercise 4.0

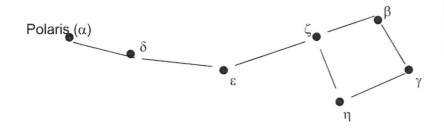

Star	Visual Magnitude (V)
Polaris (α)	2
Kocab (β)	2
γ	3.2
δ	4.5
ε	4.5
ζ	4.2
η	5

b. What is the magnitude of the faintest star visible? _____

c. Limiting magnitude for visual observing is often listed as sixth magnitude (V = 6). Why is your limiting magnitude different from this? List several things that affect limiting magnitude.

5. Use your SKYLAB2 star chart and any others you have (e.g., your text book's) to find at least 6 additional constellations.
    a. On your chart sketch in the lines connecting the stars of these constellations as has been done in the above figures.
    b. Sketch in and label the Celestial Equator on your chart.
    c. Try to locate the Ecliptic in the sky and sketch and label it on your chart.

Exercise 5.0

THE CELESTIAL HORIZON SYSTEM

I. Introduction

When we stand at most locations on the Earth, we have the distinct impression that the Earth is flat. This occurs because the curvature of the small area of the Earth usually visible is very slight. We call this "flat Earth" the **Plane of the Horizon** and divide it up into 4 quadrants, each containing 90°, by using the cardinal points of the compass. The latter are the North, South, East, and West points of the horizon. We describe things as being vertical or "straight up" if they line up with the direction of gravity at that location. It is easy for us to determine "straight up" because we have a built in mechanism for this in the inner ear (the semicircular canals). Because it seems so "natural", we build a coordinate system on these ideas called the Horizon System.

The **Celestial Horizon System** is one of the coordinate systems that astronomers find useful for locating objects in the sky. It is depicted in the Figure below.

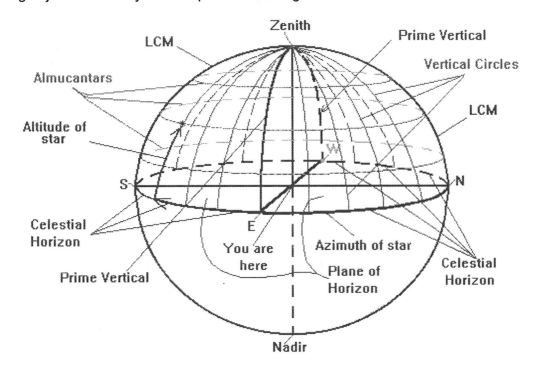

Figure 1. The above diagram is a skewed perspective, schematic diagram of the celestial sphere with circles drawn only for the half above the horizon. Circles on the far side, or western half, of the celestial sphere are drawn as dashed curves.

All the reference circles of this system do not share in the rotation of the celestial sphere and, therefore, this coordinate system is fixed with respect to a given observer. The basis for the system is the direction of gravity. We can describe this as the line from the observer on the surface of the Earth through the center of the Earth. When this line is extended out to the celestial sphere, it intersects the sky in two opposite points called the **ZENITH** and the **NADIR**. For any observer, the zenith is the point in the sky directly overhead. (The point on the celestial sphere that

Exercise 5.0

is overhead or at the zenith for you is not the same point on the celestial sphere that is overhead for someone at a different location.) The great circle halfway between the zenith and the nadir is called the **Celestial Horizon, Astronomical Horizon,** or **True Horizon** and it is the fundamental reference circle for this coordinate system. (Do not confuse the astronomical horizon with the **Visible Horizon,** the place where the earth and sky seem to meet.) See Figure 1, which shows circles drawn for only the half of the celestial sphere that is above the horizon, except for the LCM.

The Earth is extremely small compared to the size of the celestial sphere, therefore, the Earth and any observer on the Earth are to be imagined as a point at the center of the sphere. The celestial horizon is different for different observers. That is, the celestial horizon will divide the sky into different halves, depending on your geographic location on the Earth.

Now imagine a family of great circles drawn on the celestial sphere in such a way that each circle of the family passes through the zenith and nadir and crosses the horizon at a right angle. These circles are called **Vertical Circles.** You should be able to identify these circles in the above diagram.

The vertical circle that passes through the east point of the horizon, the zenith, and the west point of the horizon is called the **Prime Vertical.**

The vertical circle that connects the north point of the horizon, the zenith, and the south point of the horizon is very special and is known as the Local Celestial Meridian (LCM).

In the diagram, the LCM is the only vertical circle that lies in the plane of the paper. The Local Celestial Meridian is a reference circle that is used for measuring local time and will be referred to frequently in future exercises.

The half of the local celestial meridian (LCM) from the north celestial pole (NCP), through the zenith, to the south celestial pole (SCP) is called the upper meridian and the other half is the lower meridian. Notice that a part of the upper meridian can be below the horizon and part of the lower meridian can be above the horizon, depending on one's latitude.

Almucantars and vertical circles form a grid of intersecting circles on the celestial sphere for the celestial horizon system. This grid is analogous to that formed by the parallels of latitude and meridians of longitude on the surface of the Earth. **Remember, this system of circles is fixed with respect to an observer and does not rotate with the stars.**

II. Coordinates

The first coordinate of the horizon system (analogous to latitude on the Earth) is called **ALTITUDE.** It is the **angular distance of a point from the horizon.** The altitude is $0° 00'$ for an object that is located on the horizon and increases upwards towards the zenith. The altitude at the zenith is exactly $90°$. Negative values for altitude mean an object is below the horizon. All objects with the same altitude lie along a circle parallel to the horizon. Such a circle is often called a **parallel of altitude** or an almucantar and are labeled such in the above diagram.

The other angle of the celestial horizon system is called **AZIMUTH.** This is an angle that is measured around the celestial sphere, starting at the vertical circle passing through the **north point.** The value of the angle increases from $0°$ anywhere along this vertical circle, eastward. At the east point the azimuth is $90°$. The azimuth at the south point is $180°$ and it is $270°$ at the west point. Refer to the above diagram. The point where any vertical circle crosses the horizon has a definite azimuth, that is, it is located at a definite angular distance from the North Point of the horizon.

III. Diurnal Motion

Recall that the horizon system is fixed with respect to a given observer. Therefore, all the reference circles of this system do not share in the rotation of the celestial sphere. This means the altitude and azimuth of an object on the celestial sphere both change with time and location. Hence, this system is only useful for locating objects on the celestial sphere at a given location on the Earth and at a given instant of time

As the celestial sphere appears to turn around its axis, objects in the sky move relative to the horizon and the local celestial meridian (LCM). **The axis of rotation lies in the plane of the local celestial meridian and it is tilted relative to the celestial horizon by an amount equal to the observer's geographic latitude.**

A casual inspection of the sky reveals that all celestial objects rise on the eastern horizon, cross the local celestial meridian, where an object's altitude is a maximum, and set on the western horizon. This path that an object follows across the sky from east to west is called its **Diurnal Circle**.

> **Diurnal circles are the apparent paths that objects appear to follow as a result of the rotation of the Earth around its axis.**

Hence, the apparent rotation of the celestial sphere causes each celestial object to follow its diurnal circle. As an object moves along its diurnal circle, its altitude and azimuth in the horizon system continuously change. Since the declination of a star does not change as the Earth rotates, **an object's parallel of declination is the same as its diurnal circle**. Being able to visualize that this is so, is a necessary step in your understanding of diurnal motion. Later, we shall use the SKYLAB2 software to demonstrate the concepts that have been introduced here.

When an object crosses the upper local celestial meridian, it is said to be at **upper transit (UT)**. At upper transit the object is at its greatest distance above the horizon, that is, its altitude is a maximum. When the object crosses the lower local celestial meridian, it is said to be at **lower transit (LT)**. At **LT**, an object is at its minimum angular distance (in the algebraic sense) from the horizon. When an object is below the horizon, its angular distance from the horizon, or altitude, is assigned a negative value.

Objects make one upper transit and one lower transit each day. For an observer in the Northern Hemisphere, both upper and lower transit will occur above the horizon for stars located near the north celestial pole. Such objects will have their diurnal circles entirely above the celestial horizon and, therefore, can be seen every night. Such objects are called **circumpolar stars of perpetual apparition** (stars that are always visible) since they circle around the pole star.

By symmetry, for this same observer, there will be a range of declinations for stars near the south celestial pole that never rise above the horizon. That is, their diurnal circles are completely below the horizon and such an object can never be seen at that latitude. These stars that never rise are called **circumpolar stars of perpetual occultation**.

> **Which objects are circumpolar and which are not depends on the observer's latitude and the declination of the object.**

Objects located on the celestial equator rise exactly at the east point, while objects north or south of the celestial equator rise to the north or south of the east point. It is very important to realize that objects, which rise exactly at the east point, must set exactly at the west point. Likewise, objects that rise in the northeast set in the northwest and objects that rise in the southeast set in the southwest.

Exercise 5.0

The time that an object spends above the horizon depends essentially on where it is located with respect to the celestial equator, i.e., its declination. Half of the equator is above the horizon and so any object on it (declination $0°$) is above the horizon for 12 hours and below the horizon for 12 hours. Such an object rises at the east point and sets at the west point.

Another important angle related to diurnal motion and time is an object's **hour angle**.

Hour Angle (HA) is the angular distance of an object measured westward from the Local Celestial Meridian.

It is sometimes convenient to use positive and negative numbers to describe the position of an object with respect to the Local Celestial Meridian.

When the object is west of the Meridian, the Hour Angle is denoted as positive and when it is east of the Meridian it is negative.

The Hour Angle changes from negative to positive when the object crosses the Local Celestial Meridian, moving east to west. Note that the object's altitude at this time is a maximum and the object is said to be at **Upper Transit** (UT). The Hour Angle changes sign again when the object crosses the Local Celestial Meridian twelve hours later. At this time, the altitude of the object is a minimum and it said to be at **Lower Transit** (LT).

IV. Procedures and Tutorial

Logon to SKYLAB2 and in the main menu highlight "Celestial Sphere." This will bring up a menu of Celestial Sphere programs. Now highlight "Diurnal Motion" and press Enter. This generates on the monitor screen an exterior, 3D, perspective-view of the celestial sphere, looking from east towards west. Note the following:

The **Celestial Horizon** (CH) is the white horizontal circle connecting the points **N, E, S, & W.**

The **Axis of Rotation** is the dark blue line that connects the celestial poles, NCP and SCP. Note that it is tilted at an angle with respect to the horizon. This angle depends on the observer's latitude.

The **Celestial Equator** (CE) is the red circle that is slanted with respect to the Horizon and it lies in a plane that is perpendicular to the axis. The Celestial Equator passes through the East and West points of the Horizon for every observer, regardless of latitude or longitude.

The **Local Celestial Meridian** (LCM) is represented by the light blue circle. It passes through the North Point of the Horizon, the North Celestial Pole (NCP), the Zenith, the South Point of the Horizon, and the Nadir.

The green line connecting the zenith and nadir is perpendicular to the plane of the horizon.

By default, an object with a declination of $0°$ is shown moving along the Celestial Equator. This object is said to be executing its **Diurnal Motion** or to be moving along its **Diurnal Circle.** This motion is said to be due to the rotation of the celestial sphere and is really a reflection of the

Earth's rotation on its axis. The object is yellow when it is on the front side of the celestial sphere, but it becomes a dashed open circle when it moves to the rear or backside of the celestial sphere. Watch this taking place.

In the upper left of the screen, the observer's latitude and the declination of the moving object are given. In the lower right corner of the screen, the instantaneous value for the object's hour angle is given.

Now press the space bar to stop the diurnal motion. The altitude and azimuth of the object now appear to the lower left of the screen. Take note of where the object is in the horizon system and try to reconcile this position in your mind with the values that have just been displayed. Now hit the space bar again and the diurnal motion will continue. Stop the motion again at some other position and again compare the altitude and azimuth that is displayed with the position of the object. **Note that the altitude is negative when the object is below the celestial horizon.**

Because the moving object has a declination of exactly $0°$, it rises exactly at the East Point of the horizon, and therefore, its azimuth is $90°$. Because of the skewed perspective of the diagram, the animation does not show an object to be exactly on the horizon when the computer displays its altitude to be $0°$. This is a problem with the software and one must learn to allow for this. Note and remember:

When an object just rises or sets, its altitude must be zero degrees.

Now try to stop the object as it just rises, transits the Local Celestial Meridian, or sets. You may have to make several attempts at this to be successful. If you are not successful, it is possible to slow the motion down in two ways:

1. Type "O" for Options and a window menu will drop down from the top of the screen. Highlight the option "Step", and then press the Enter key. The current value for the "step" is then shown and should be $00^d\ 00^h\ 14^m$ (Note there are no seconds.) This is the default value for **Step**, which is the time interval between the positions that the computer calculates and displays on the monitor screen to animate its motion. Tab over to the 14^m and change it to 05^m. **Be careful to pay attention to the different column headings identifying days, hours, and minutes.** Now hit the Enter key. Since the computer must now compute more positions to animate the diurnal motion of the object, it will run slower. You may want to experiment with different Step times.

2. Type "O" for Options and highlight "Delay" in the drop-down window menu, then press the Enter key. Increase the Delay time to 0.70 seconds. Hit the Enter key. The computer now waits this amount of time before displaying the object's next position along its diurnal circle, thereby slowing down the motion.

The first method has the advantage of presenting more closely spaced positions of the object along the diurnal circle. You may decide how to use both methods to your advantage. If you miss stopping the object exactly where it was supposed to be stopped, it is not necessary to wait for it to go all the way around again. *The left cursor key is like a rewind key. As long as you hold it down, the diurnal motion will be reversed at a higher speed. Similarly, the right cursor key is a fast forward key. Try these out.*

V. Assignment

Type "L" to change the latitude and set it to exactly $40°$ N. Keep the declination of the object to be animated at $0°$. Allow the diurnal motion to continue at a rate that you determined above to be convenient for you to stop the object at any point along its diurnal circle. When you have

Exercise 5.0

successfully stopped the above object at the point where it rises, you are to record the altitude, azimuth, and hour angle on the worksheet on the first line. You have succeeded in stopping the object at the right place only if the computer gives a value of 0°, which may be slightly different than what your eye tells you. Always use the following rule:

For any object to be rising or setting, its altitude must be zero.

Do not use Hour Angle as a criterion for determining when a star rises or sets. What the hour angle is when an object rises or sets depends on its declination and your latitude.

When recording angles, drop the number of arcseconds and record your answers in degrees and arcminutes, like this: 0° 15' or 32° 46'. Do not use the colons. If you are not able to stop an object at exactly 0° 00' altitude when it rises or sets, record the closest value to zero that you can get.

Be sure to set your step size and delay times to values that permit you to work within tolerances < 30' for altitude and < 0.02 hours for hour angle.

Now allow the diurnal motion to continue, and try to stop the object (for Dec.=0°) when it crosses the Local Celestial Meridian (**LCM**) at maximum altitude. Recall that this event is called **Upper Transit (UT)**. Note:

The hour angle should read exactly 0.00 when an object is at upper transit.

Again, try to stop the object when its hour angle is as close to 0.00 as you can and record the value of the star's altitude, azimuth, and hour angle on the next line of the worksheet.

Next, stop the object exactly at the point where its sets. This will now be when the top of the ball is just below the West point of the celestial horizon, but the real criterion is when the computer readout for the altitude is exactly zero. Again, record the values you get on the worksheet.

Now continue the diurnal motion until the object is at lower transit on the Celestial Meridian. Recall that **Lower Transit** (LT) is when an object crosses the **LCM** at minimum altitude. Whether lower transit is above or below the horizon depends on both the observer's latitude and the declination of the object. In any event:

The hour angle should be either +12 or -12, for an object to be at lower transit.

Try stopping the object exactly at this hour angle and record the requested coordinates on the worksheet.

Now you will investigate the diurnal motion for objects with other declinations. *The declination can be changed by using the cursor-up or down keys. If you hold down the cursor-up key the declination will increase.* You should watch the value change in the upper left corner of the screen until it is the value you want. *The cursor down key is used to decrease the declination.*

You are to repeat the above measurements for the objects with declinations 25° and 65°, but first review the criteria for rising, setting, and making transit of the meridian before proceeding to another declination.

You will find that some stars do not rise or set but have their diurnal circles either entirely above or below the Celestial Horizon. Recall that such stars are called **Circumpolar Stars** and

should be identified as such on the lines for rising and s.
find that at any latitude other than the equator or pole, there
set, and make lower transit at the same point on the horizon ai.
the southern-most circumpolar stars for that latitude and they h.
above the horizon.

In addition to latitude 40° N, repeat all of the above procedures for anu
by your instructor. For the second latitude, the declination 20⁰ replaces declinati.

To change the latitude, type "L" for the latitude window menu to drop down and the
Enter key. Type in the value of the latitude you want. Be sure to change the fields for ar.
and arcseconds to zero, such as, **65:00:00.**

Use a different worksheet for each of the two latitudes you investigate. The latitude should be
written in the space at the top of the worksheet.

**From what you have learned through the above investigations, try to determine
generalized answers to the questions at the bottom of the worksheet that are valid for any
latitude.**

The data that you have obtained in this exercise will be used in Exercise 6.0, where you will
learn how to draw diurnal circles.

HORIZON SYSTEM ANSWER SHEET

Latitude: _____

Declination	Position	Hour Angle (decimal hours)	Altitude (deg. & arcmin.)	Azimuth (deg. & arcmin.)
0°	Rises			
0°	UT			
0°	Sets			
0°	LT			
25°	Rises			
25°	UT			
25°	Sets			
25°	LT			
65°	Rises			
65°	UT			
65°	Sets			
65°	LT			

To answer the following questions, vary the declination until the condition is satisfied as seen from this latitude:

1. What is the declination of an object that makes UT at the zenith? [   ]

2. What is the declination of an object that makes LT at the north point of the horizon? [   ]

3. What is the declination of the southern most star that can be observed from this latitude? [   ]

4. At what declination do objects begin to have diurnal circles that are entirely above the celestial horizon? [   ]

HORIZON SYSTEM ANSWER SHEET

Latitude: _____

Declination	Position	Hour Angle (decimal hours)	Altitude (deg. & arcmin.)	Azimuth (deg. & arcmin.)
0⁰	Rises			
0⁰	UT			
0⁰	Sets			
0⁰	LT			
20⁰	Rises			
20⁰	UT			
20⁰	Sets			
20⁰	LT			
65⁰	Rises			
65⁰	UT			
65⁰	Sets			
65⁰	LT			

To answer the following questions, vary the declination until the condition is satisfied as seen from this latitude:

1. What is the declination of an object that makes UT at the zenith? ▢

2. What is the declination of an object that makes LT at the north point of the horizon? ▢

3. What is the declination of the southern most star that can be observed from this latitude? ▢

4. At what declination do objects begin to have diurnal circles that are entirely above the celestial horizon? ▢

Exercise 5.2

MEASURING ALTITUDE AND AZIMUITH

I. Introduction

One should review the horizon system as described in Exercise 5.0 before proceeding to do this exercise. It is assumed you are familiar with the definitions for altitude and azimuth and all the other terms pertaining to the horizon system.

To the right, Fig. 1 is a diagram representing a generic horizon system. By this is meant there is no specification of latitude or time. The principles and concepts that will be utilized in this exercise are valid for any latitude.

Consider the star A shown in Fig. 1. This star is assumed to be located on the front, or eastern, half of the celestial sphere. It is desired to find the altitude and azimuth of this star. A protractor can not be used to directly measure either of these angles, for the plane of the protractor must be in the plane containing the two lines of sight that define the angle. Since the protractor may be used only in the plane of this page, the angle would have to be an arc lying along a circle in the plane of the page. The only such circle shown in all the diagrams is the local celestial meridian. This circle connects the points N, Z, & S. Since star A is not located on this circle, we can not measure its altitude or azimuth directly. However, azimuth can be estimated and altitude can be measured indirectly.

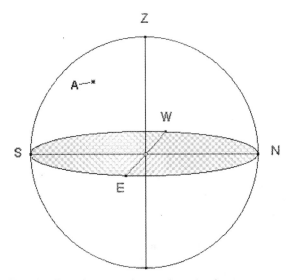

Fig. 1. Star A shown located on the front or eastern half of the celestial sphere in a generic horizon system.

We proceed as follows: First we draw the vertical circle of the star as shown in Fig. 2. Note that the vertical circle is drawn from the zenith, through the star, crosses the celestial horizon at a right angle, and then continues to the nadir point. Where the vertical circle intersects the celestial horizon indicates the azimuth of the star. This can not be measured with a protractor but must be estimated as follows:

Azimuth is measured from the north point of the horizon, eastward along the horizon to the vertical circle of a star. At the East point of the horizon, the azimuth would be exactly 90° and at the South point of the horizon, the azimuth would be 180°. Halfway between the East point and South point the azimuth would be 135°. Allowances for foreshortening in the diagram must be made to get a more precise value. When this is done, the azimuth for the star is about 120°. This

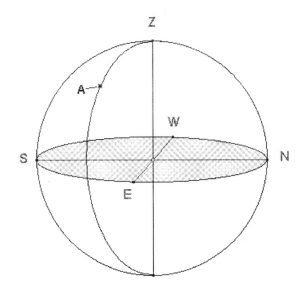

Fig. 2. This diagram shows the vertical circle for star A.

estimate probably has an error of about ±7°, but this is the best that can be done.

To determine the altitude, a more precise value can be measured. First one must draw the parallel of altitude for the star as shown below in Fig. 3. Note that the parallel of altitude is in a plane parallel to the plane of the celestial horizon. Any star located on this parallel has the same altitude. Therefore a star on this parallel, and on the local celestial meridian, would have the same altitude as the star A.

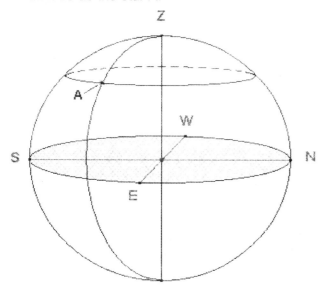

Fig. 3. In this diagram, the parallel of altitude has been added for star A.

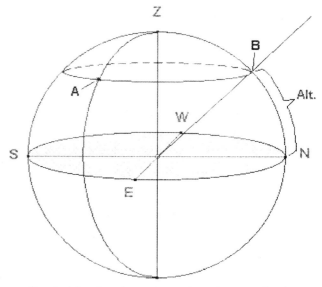

Fig. 4. A line has been drawn for using a protractor to measure the altitude of the star A.

In the next diagram, Fig. 4, a star B is drawn on the same parallel of altitude as star A. Star B is also on the local celestial meridian. A line is drawn from the center of the celestial sphere to such a hypothetical star, B. (The line has been extended beyond B to facilitate measuring the angle with a protractor.) The altitude of star B is indicated as the arc along the local celestial meridian from the north point of the horizon to the hypothetical star B. Remember, the altitude of star B is the same as the altitude of star A. This angle may now be measured with a protractor by aligning the bottom of the protractor along the line connecting the N and S points of the celestial horizon. You should use your protractor on Fig. 4 to do this now. Be sure to use the scale of the protractor that has 0 starting at the point **N**.

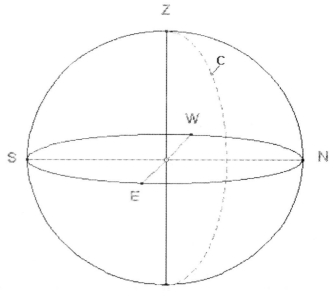

Fig. 5. The vertical circle for star C, which is assumed to be on the back, or western half of the celestial sphere is drawn as a dashed semicircle from the zenith to the nadir.

When given a problem of this nature one must take into consideration whether the star is located on the front half of the celestial sphere or the back half. A star on the back part or western half of the celestial sphere is depicted as star C in Figure 5. The vertical circle through star C is now drawn as a dashed curve, to indicate that it is located on the back, or western, half of the celestial sphere. The point where this vertical circle intersects the celestial horizon is now between the **W** and **N** points of the horizon. Therefore, an estimate for the azimuth of this star would be 285°. The parallel of altitude for this star must be

34

Exercise 5.2

drawn so that the star is located on the dashed portion of such a circle. This has been done in Fig. 6 below.

To measure the altitude of the star, draw a line from the center of the celestial sphere to a point where the parallel of altitude of star C intersects the local celestial meridian, similar to what was drawn for star A in Fig. 4. This is also shown in Fig. 6. This time, a star D, located at azimuth 180°, was used to show that it does not matter on what part of the local celestial meridian the star with the same altitude as C is located. Now take your protractor and measure the altitude of the star labeled D.

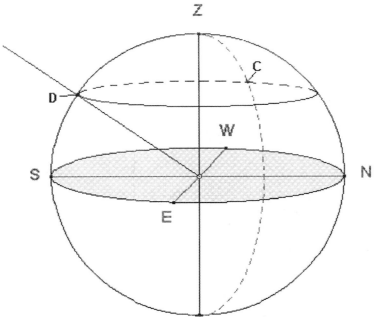

Fig. 6. This diagram shows the parallel of altitude drawn for the star C. The star D has the same altitude as C and a line has been drawn for measuring this altitude with a protractor.

On the answer sheet for this exercise there are 2 celestial sphere diagrams. On each of these diagrams, there are located 2 stars. For each diagram, draw the vertical circle and parallel of altitude for each star as shown in the examples above. Make sure that any circle that is drawn for the western half of the celestial sphere is drawn with dashes. Then use a protractor to measure the altitude and estimate the azimuth of the star. Write your results in the appropriate spaces.

EXERCISE 5.2 ANSWER SHEET

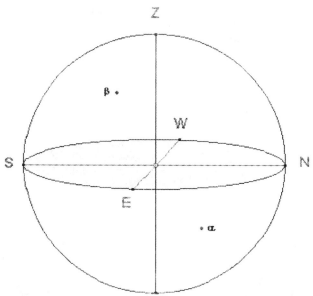

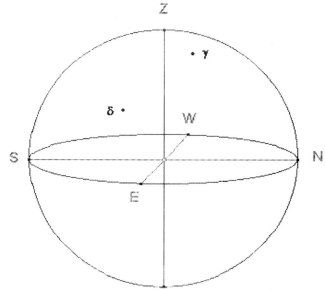

Draw the parallel of altitude and vertical circle for each of the stars in the above diagram. Assume α is on the eastern half of the celestial sphere and β is on the western half of the celestial sphere. Then determine the altitude and azimuth of each star and record.

Determine the altitude and azimuth of the stars γ and δ as in the diagram to the left. The star γ is on the eastern half of the celestial sphere while δ is on the western half.

Star α: Altitude: _____   Azimuth: _____

Star β: Altitude: _____   Azimuth: _____

Star γ: Altitude: _____   Azimuth: _____

Star δ: Altitude: _____   Azimuth: _____

Exercise 6.0

DIURNAL MOTIONS AND CIRCLES

I. Orientation of the Equatorial System within the Horizon System

Figure I depicts the Earth with its axis of rotation shown vertical and its geographic equator shown lying in a horizontal plane that is perpendicular to the axis. IF an observer is located at point **A**, their latitude is indicated by the angle phi (ϕ). A line drawn from the center of the Earth, through the observer at A, and then continued upwards towards the celestial sphere, points to the observer's zenith, which is labeled Z_A in the figure. A similar line is drawn for an observer standing at point **B**, with latitude beta (β), pointing to their zenith which is labeled Z_B and for an observer at **C**, with latitude gamma (γ), whose zenith is labeled Z_C. It should be clear that the zenith is located at a different point on the celestial sphere for different observers.

A line through A, tangent to the Earth lies in the plane of the observer's horizon and indicates the directions to the north and south points (labeled NPH & SPH in the figure) of the horizon. Similar remarks are true for the hypothetical observers at B and C. Clearly, the half of the sky that is above an observer's celestial horizon is different for different observers.

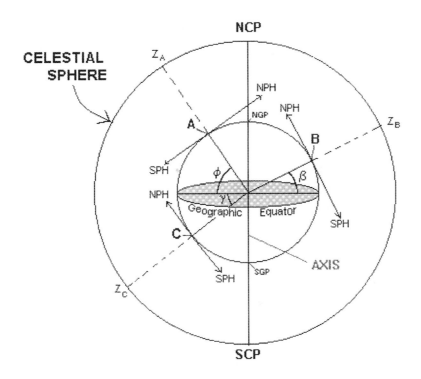

Fig, 1. A schematic diagram showing how the location of an observer's zenith and nader in their sky depends on latitude.

Figure 2 depicts the Earth with the shaded plane of the geographic equator drawn midway between the north geographic pole and the south geographic pole (labeled NGP & SGP). The line drawn connecting the geographical poles is the axis of rotation of the Earth. A celestial hemisphere, reduced in size to fit in the diagram, is drawn centered on an observer who is located somewhere near mid-latitude in the Northern Hemisphere. A line is drawn through the

Exercise 6.0

observer parallel to the Earth's axis of rotation. Since parallel lines may be considered to indicate the same point on the celestial sphere, both of these lines indicate the direction of the north celestial pole (labeled NCP in the figure). Although the NCP is shown in the figure to be two separate points, they are actually the same place in the sky as seen by the observer. Similar geometric remarks may be applied to show that the plane of geographic equator and the plane of the celestial equator, as labeled in the diagram, lie in the same plane as seen by the observer.

By definition, the angle between the observer and the geographic equator is the observer's latitude, labeled as ϕ. The point on the celestial sphere over the observer's head is the zenith (Z), and the point under foot on the other side of the celestial sphere is the nadir.

Using some plane geometry, it is easy to show that the observer would see the north celestial pole (NCP) located at an angle above the North Point of the horizon equal to the observers latitude (ϕ). This geometric argument is shown in the lower right of Fig. 2.

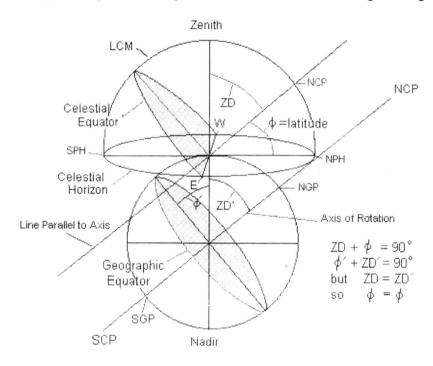

Figure 2. A schematic diagram showing why the altitude of the NCP for an observer is equal to the observer's latitude

Now imagine yourself in Figure 1, standing at the north geographic pole (latitude 90° N.). The north celestial pole (NCP) would have an altitude of 90° and, therefore, be at your zenith. The celestial equator and celestial horizon would coincide.

Now picture yourself on the Earth's equator, at 0° latitude. Here the celestial equator would pass through your zenith and the north celestial pole (NCP) would lie at the North Point of the horizon and have an altitude of 0°.   Hence, the following general rule:

THE ALTITUDE OF THE NORTH CELESTIAL POLE IN DEGREES IS ALWAYS NUMERICALLY EQUAL TO THE LATITUDE OF THE OBSERVER.

Also, for any observer located in the northern hemisphere of the Earth, the north celestial pole (NCP) is always a point located on the local celestial meridian, between the zenith and the north point of the horizon. Since the LCM is also the vertical circle connecting the zenith and the north point of the horizon, and azimuth is measured from the latter point eastward, the azimuth of the north celestial pole (NCP) is always equal to $0°$.

II. Diurnal Motion

Because of the Earth's rotation, objects appear to move along paths around the sky from east to west. These daily paths that objects trace across the sky are known as **diurnal circles**. Since the sky appears to turn around the celestial poles and parallel to the celestial equator, a diurnal circle is actually the same as the object's parallel of declination. Thus all objects with the same declination trace out the same diurnal circle. A few of these circles are shown in Figure 3.

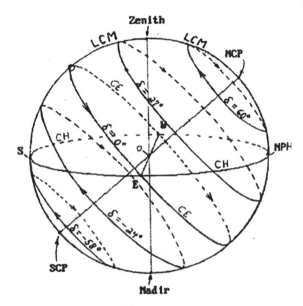

Figure 3. Diurnal circles drawn on the celestial sphere for several different declinations, as seen from latitude 40° N.

Notice that these circles make an angle with the horizon but they are all parallel to one another. From the geometry of the situation, it can be shown that the celestial equator (CE) intersects an observer's celestial horizon at the east and west points. Thus the diurnal circle that passes through the east point of the horizon and west point of the horizon is the celestial equator (CE). Recall that every point on the celestial equator is $90°$ from either of the two celestial poles. Therefore, the angle that the celestial equator makes with the horizon is always equal to $90°$ minus the observer's latitude ($90° - \phi$).

Furthermore, from Fig. 2 the following geometric relationship may be deduced:

THE CELESTIAL EQUATOR INTERSECTS THE LOCAL CELESTIAL MERIDIAN AT ANGLE BELOW THE ZENITH NUMERICALLY EQUAL TO THE LATITUDE.

This is a corollary to the previous general rule about the altitude of the north celestial pole.

Recall from Exercise 5.0, that the time that an object spends above the horizon depends essentially on where it is located with respect to the celestial equator, i.e., its declination. Half of the equator is above the horizon and so any object on it (declination $0°$) is above the horizon for 12 hours and below the horizon for 12 hours. Such an object rises at the east point and sets at the west point.

Exercise 6.0

Those objects with declinations between 0° and +90°, that are not circumpolar stars, rise in the northeast, remain above the horizon for more than twelve hours and set in the northwest. Those objects with declinations between 0° and -90°, that are not circumpolar stars, rise and set, in the southeast, are above the horizon for less than twelve hours and set in the southwest.

A star always rises and sets at the same place on the horizon and is above the horizon for the same amount of time every day of the year. This is not true, however, for the Sun, Moon, and planets, because these objects move with respect to the background stars, i.e., their declination changes with time. Twice a year the Sun crosses the equator and has a declination of 0°. It then rises at the east point and there are twelve hours of daylight and twelve hours of darkness. These two events occur about March 21 and September 21 (the days of the vernal and autumnal equinoxes).

In the summer the Sun is north of the celestial equator (has a + declination) and rises in the northeast. It is above the horizon for more than 12 hours and the daylight portion of the day is long. During the winter the Sun is below the celestial equator (has a negative declination). It then rises in the southeast and sets in the southwest, and the amount of daylight is less than 12 hours. The day of the year with the longest daylight period occurs about June 21 (the day of the summer solstice). The day of the year with the shortest amount of daylight occurs about December 21 (the day of the winter solstice). These concepts are explored more fully in exercise 7.0

III. Tutorial Using SKYLAB2.

Logon to SKYLAB2 and select "**4 Celestial Sphere**" from the main menu. From the Celestial Sphere options menu, select *Diurnal Motion*. After you press the enter key, a representation of the celestial sphere will be drawn on the monitor screen showing the equatorial system superimposed within the horizon system. The default latitude is 40° 16' 15" N. The latitude is displayed in the upper left corner of the screen. Look at the altitude of the north celestial pole (NCP) and confirm that this is the same as the latitude. Use you protractor to do this.

Also note that the azimuth of the north celestial pole (NCP) is 0°. Now locate the point where the celestial equator (CE) and the local celestial meridian (LCM) intersect. Use your protractor to confirm that this point is located at an angular distance below the zenith equal to the observer's latitude.

An object with 0° declination (the default value) will be on the celestial equator and appear to move in a circle around the axis while staying on the celestial equator (CE). This is an animation of the diurnal rotation of the celestial sphere for this object relative to the observer. Therefore, this object's diurnal circle (DC) is the celestial equator itself. Note that this object's diurnal circle is cut exactly in half by the celestial horizon; this will be true at all latitudes for the celestial equator.

Now change the latitude to 25° N. To change the latitude, type "L" to pull down the latitude change menu. You may also change declination by typing "D" to get that menu. Now note again that the altitude of the north celestial pole (NCP) is equal to the observer's latitude and that the azimuth of the north celestial pole (NCP) is still zero. Note that the inclination of the celestial equator with respect to the horizon changes, but that it still passes through the East and West points of the horizon. Also check the zenith distance of the point where the celestial equator and local celestial meridian (LCM) intersect.

Change the latitude now to 0° and note the changes. You should also explore other latitudes, such as 65° and 90° and note the relationships mentioned above. These relationships do not depend on longitude!

We shall now explore diurnal circles for different declinations and latitudes. If you want to slow down or speed up the diurnal motion, type "O" for the options window. Here you may select to change the step size or the delay time. Making the step size smaller will slow down the motion; experiment with different values for the step size. Changing the delay time to a larger value will slow down the motion as well. A good delay time is 0.75 seconds.

Now return to 40° N latitude. Use the up-arrow cursor key to change the declination to 20°. The value of the declination is shown in the upper left corner of the screen, as is the observer's latitude. The hour angle of the object is shown at the lower right corner of the screen. Notice the change in the object's diurnal circle compared with what it was at declination 0°. Note that it is still a circle around the axis and parallel to the celestial equator, but slanted with respect to the celestial horizon. Remember that the amount of this slant depends on the latitude of the observer. Note also that more of the diurnal circle is above the horizon than below.

Now continue to use the cursor-up key to increase the declination until the diurnal circle is one that carries the object through the zenith. The declination where this happens should be equal to the latitude. Is this diurnal circle entirely above the horizon?

Continue to change the declination until the object just touches the north point of the horizon at lower transit. At what declination does this occur? It should be 90° minus the latitude. This will always be true and such a star would be the star with the lowest declination that has its diurnal circle entirely above the celestial horizon. In other words, this is the southernmost **circumpolar star of perpetual apparition** (stars that never set).

Now find the declination of the star that just touches the South point of the horizon at upper transit. This will be the declination for the northernmost **circumpolar star of perpetual occultation** (stars that never rise).

Now you should explore other declinations, including negative values (use the down-arrow key), in order to visualize how diurnal circles depend on the declination. You should repeat all of the above for different latitudes to see how diurnal circles depend on both latitude and declination.

IV. Assignment

There are three answer sheets for this exercise. Each one depicts the celestial sphere as seen at three specific latitudes. Select the two diagrams from this exercise that match the latitudes for which you collected data on the worksheets of Exercise 5.0. One of these must be 40°. Follow the directions below to help you draw on these answer diagrams, the diurnal circles for each of the objects of different declination for which you have data from Exercise 5.0. The diurnal circle for declination 0°, the celestial equator is already drawn. The data from Exercise 5.0 will also be used to assist you in drawing the diurnal circles and to annotate your diagrams. Don't forget to annotate the same points on the celestial equator also. Your results should look similar to the example drawn for an object of declination -30° on the chart for latitude 40°.

For your first try; draw lightly with a pencil using the computer animation to help you. When you have finished for all the declinations at each of the latitudes, draw your final rendition. **Use only a pencil,** so that you can erase any mistakes; you might want to color code the circles by declination. While drawing diurnal circles, proceed as follows:

1. Use the declination of the star and your protractor to locate the upper transit (UT) and lower transit (LT) points on the local celestial meridian (LCM). To do this, set the zero line of the protractor along the line connecting the two points where the celestial equator crosses the LCM and measure the declination angle from those points. Make sure your marks are on the LCM, label these marks, and then connect them with a faint straight line. Check the altitudes of these points using your protractor. The values should agree closely with those you recorded on the data sheet from Exercise 5.0.

2. Note the point where the north-south line intersects the line you drew in step 1. Through this point, draw a faint guideline parallel to the east-west line, from the eastern horizon to the western horizon. This line determines the points on the horizon where the object rises and sets. Label each of these two points accordingly.

3. Draw a solid, concave curve from the upper transit (UT) point to the lower transit (LT) point and through the **rise-point** to represent the half of the diurnal circle on the front side of the celestial sphere. Try to keep this curve symmetrical about the axis of rotation (the line connecting the celestial poles).

Exercise 6.0

4. Now draw a dashed, concave curve from upper transit (UT) to lower transit (LT) and through the **set-point** to represent the half of the diurnal circle on the backside of the celestial sphere.
5. Indicate the direction of diurnal motion with a short arrow on the front half of the diurnal circle and another on the back half of the diurnal circle. See how this is done on the sample diurnal circle drawn for declination -30° on the chart for latitude 40° N.
6. Indicate the declination of the diurnal circle somewhere along the circle like this: $\delta = +25°$. Again, refer to the sample diurnal circle drawn for declination -30°.
7. Write the corresponding altitude, azimuth, and hour angle near the points where the star rises, sets, makes upper transit (UT), and lower transit (LT). For the altitude and azimuth, give values to the nearest arcminute only; like this: Alt = 30° 42'. For the hour angle, give the values in hours and decimal parts thereof, e.g., HA = 5^h.32.
8. **Don't forget to do this for the celestial equator also.**

In general your diurnal circles should adhere to the following properties:

1. They are circles centered on the axis of rotation.
2. They are circles lying in planes parallel to the plane of the celestial equator.
3. The points of upper and lower transit must be on the celestial meridian and symmetrically positioned on either side of the celestial poles.
4. The rise and set points must lie along a line parallel to the east-west line and in the plane of the celestial horizon.

It is important that the diurnal circles that you draw look like the ones shown in Fig. 3 and the sample one already drawn on the answer chart for latitude 40°, including all the annotations.

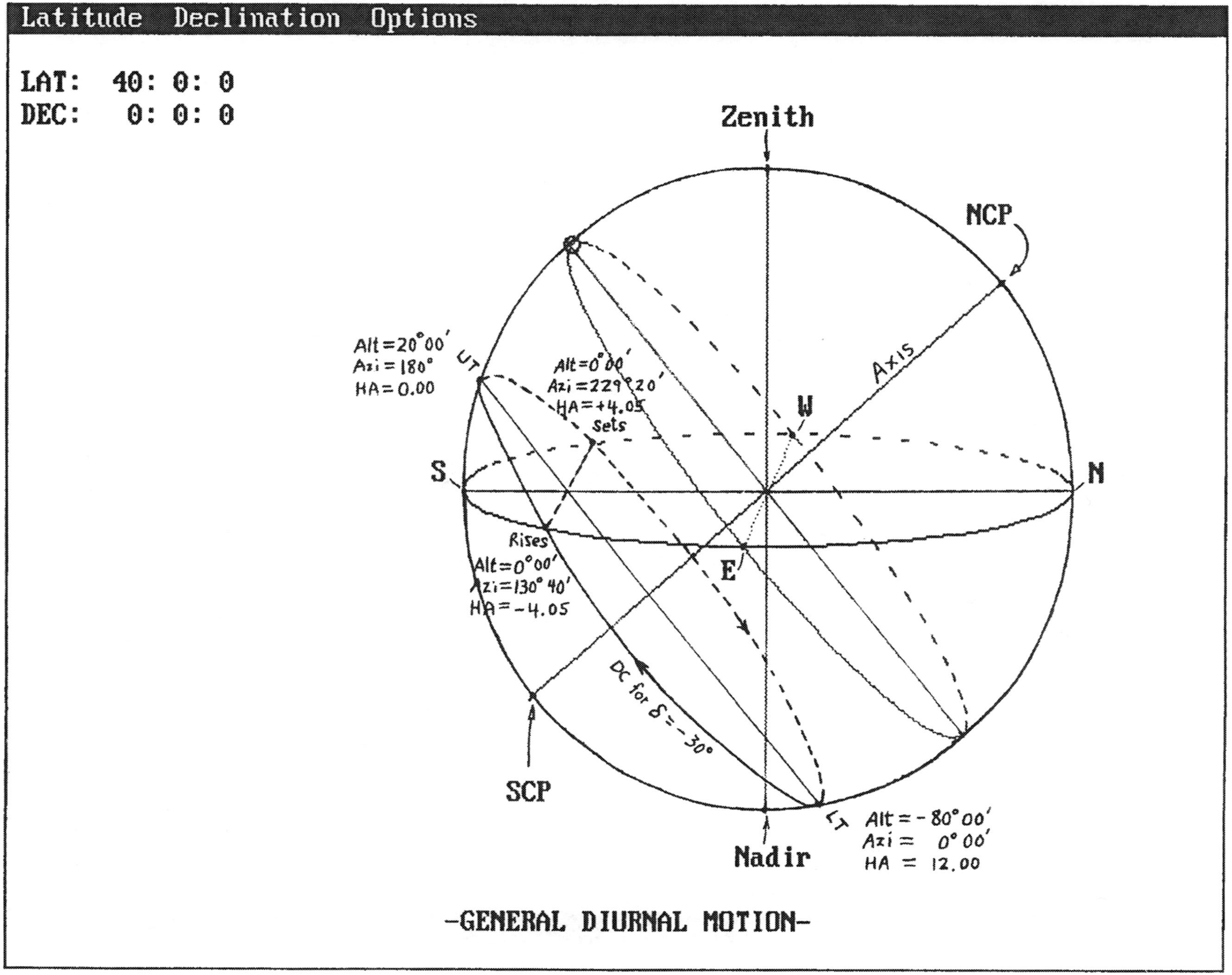

Latitude Declination Options

LAT: 40: 0: 0
DEC: 0: 0: 0

N

NCP

Zenith

Axis

W

E

Alt = -80°00'
Azi =   0°00'
HA = 12.00

Nadir

DC for δ = -30°

Alt = 0°00'
Azi = 229°20
HA = +4.05
Sets

Alt = 0°00'
Azi = 130°40'
HA = -4.05
Rises

SCP

Alt = 20°00'
Azi = 180°
HA = 0.00

S

—GENERAL DIURNAL MOTION—

43

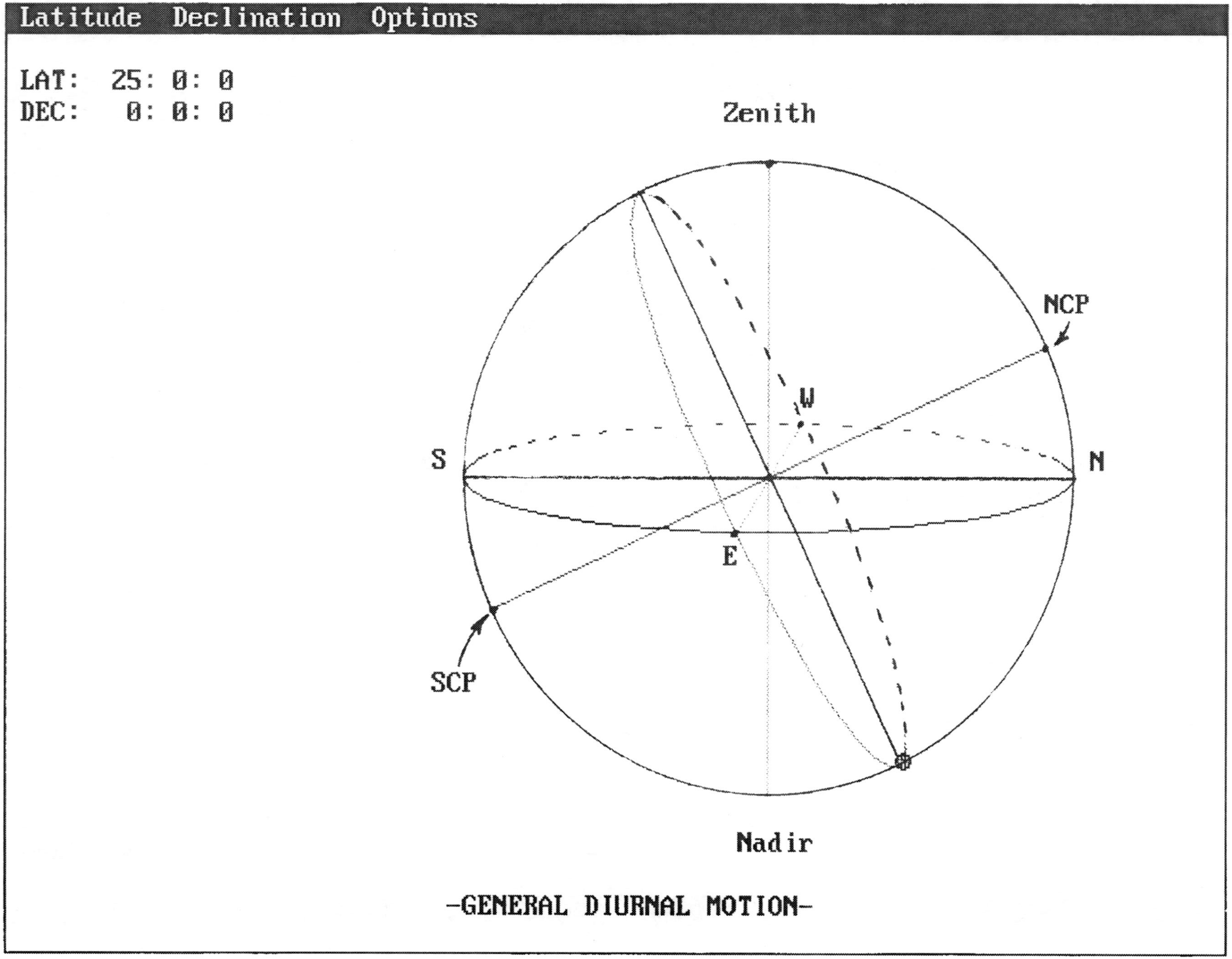

Latitude Declination Options
LAT: 25: 0: 0
DEC: 0: 0: 0
Zenith
NCP
W
S
N
E
SCP
Nadir
-GENERAL DIURNAL MOTION-

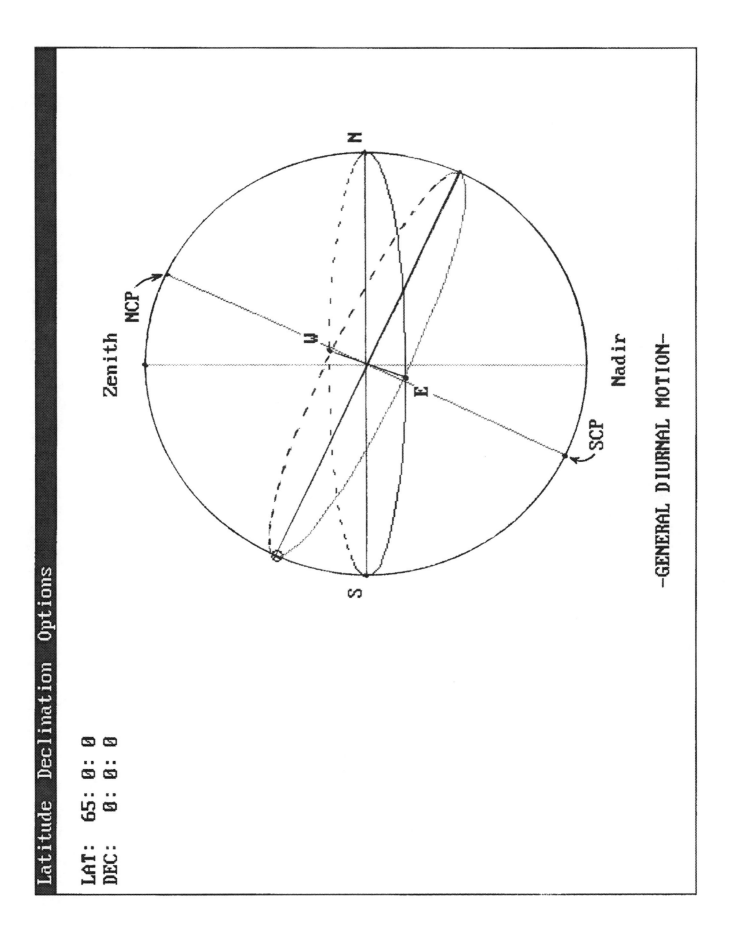

Latitude Declination Options

LAT: 65: 0: 0
DEC: 0: 0: 0

Zenith

NCP

N

W

E

S

SCP

Nadir

—GENERAL DIURNAL MOTION—

45

Exercise 7.0

THE CHANGING DIURNAL CIRCLES OF THE SUN

I. The Apparent Annual Motion of the Sun

A star always rises and sets at the same place on the horizon and, hence, it is above the horizon for the same amount of time every day of the year. That is, a star traces out the same diurnal circle every day because its declination does not change. This is not true for the Sun, Moon, and planets. Near mid-latitude in the summer, the Sun rises in the northeast and sets in the northwest, with the daylight portion of the day longer than the nighttime portion. During the winter, the Sun rises in the southeast and sets in the southwest, with the amount of daylight hours less than the amount of nighttime hours. Twice a year the Sun rises exactly at the East Point of the horizon and sets exactly at the West Point. On these two days, there are twelve hours of sunlight and twelve hours of darkness. These two events occur about March 21 and September 22 and the Sun is then located at the **Vernal** or **Autumnal Equinox** points in the sky. The day of the year with the longest daylight period occurs about June 21, when the Sun is at the **Summer Solstice**. The day of the year with the shortest amount of daylight occurs about December 22, when the Sun is at the **Winter Solstice**. These things are related to the fact that the diurnal circle of the Sun slowly changes from one day to the next, which means the declination of the Sun changes slowly throughout the year.

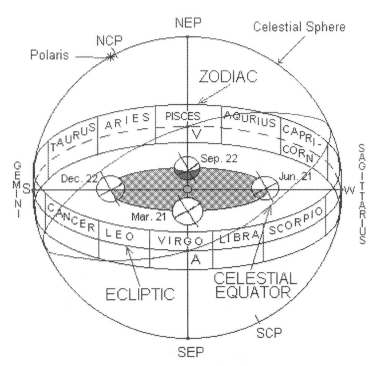

Figure 1. The relationship between the plane of the Earth's orbit, the ecliptic, the Zodiac, and the celestial equator. The position of the Earth in its orbit around the Sun is shown for four important seasonal dates of the year.

The changing declination and right ascension of the Sun is caused by the fact that Earth revolves in orbit around the Sun with its axis of rotation tilted with respect to the plane of its orbit. The amount of this tilt is 23.5° as measured from a line perpendicular to the Earth's orbital plane. This line pierces the celestial sphere at two points called the **north ecliptic pole and south ecliptic pole.** In Figure 1, these two points are designated as **NEP** and **SEP**.

Exercise 7.0

As the Earth revolves in orbit, its axis of rotation remains parallel to itself. That is, the axis always points towards the north celestial pole (**NCP**). For an observer on the Earth, the Sun appears to move in a circle around the celestial sphere eastward with respect to the **fixed stars.** This circle is called the **ecliptic** and is labeled VSAW in Fig. 1. Note that the ecliptic lies in the plane of the Earth's orbit. Thus the ecliptic is inclined to the celestial equator by 23.5°. This angle is referred to as the **obliquity of the ecliptic.** Therefore, as the Sun appears to move around the ecliptic over the course of a year, its angular distance from the celestial equator (declination) changes. The 2 points of intersection of the ecliptic and the celestial equator are called the **equinoxes**.

Now, the Earth takes 365.2422 days to complete a 360° orbit around the Sun. Therefore:

In the sky, the Sun appears to move eastward along the ecliptic
about one degree per day, relative to the "fixed stars."

This apparent motion of the Sun is merely a reflection of the Earth's revolution. On or about March 21, the Sun crosses the celestial equator moving from south to north. The Sun is then at the point labeled V in Figure 1, which is called the vernal equinox. The Sun reaches its maximum northerly declination (+23.5°) on or about June 21. It is then at the point labeled S, which is called the **summer solstice.** The point where the Sun reaches its maximum southerly declination (-23.5°) is the **winter solstice,** W.

The equinoxes and solstices are associated with the above dates only in the sense that the Sun is located at these points on or about those dates. Actually these dates may change by a few days from one year to another. The equinoxes and solstices should be thought of as positions on the celestial sphere rather than as specific dates. For example, the vernal equinox is a point on the celestial sphere located in the constellation of stars called Pisces. Like other points on the celestial sphere, an observer on the Earth sees the solstices and equinoxes to execute diurnal circles that depend on the declination of these points. The vernal equinox rises at the east point of the horizon and sets at the west point of the horizon every day throughout the year. Hence, when the Sun is at the vernal equinox, it also rises at the east point and sets at the west point. The daily motion of the Sun is discussed in more detail in the next section.

The following table lists the declinations and right ascensions for some important points in the sky. A "**U**" means undefined. Note that objects on the celestial equator have declinations of zero degrees and that objects south of the celestial equator have negative declinations.

A TABLE OF SOME DECLINATIONS AND RIGHT ASCENSIONS

POINT	DECLINATION (Degrees)	RIGHT ASCENSION (Hours)
VE	0.00	0.00
SS	+23.5	6.00
AE	0.00	12.00
WS	- 23.5	18.00
NCP	+90.00	U
SCP	- 90.00	U

The right ascension and declination of the Sun's position vary as it moves along the ecliptic from one point to another as shown in the above table. The time required for the Sun to cycle through its coordinates, that is, the time it takes the Sun to go once around the ecliptic from the vernal equinox back to the vernal equinox is called the **year of the seasons or tropical year.** The Moon cycles through its coordinates in about one month. The time required for a planet to do this depends on its period of revolution.

Because the orbits of the planets of our Solar System lie nearly in the same plane as the Earth's orbit, the planetary orbits are circles in the sky close to the ecliptic. The belt of the sky, centered on the ecliptic and where most of the planets are observed, is called the **zodiac**. The ancients organized the stars that are located in this belt into twelve constellations known as the **zodiacal constellations**. The Sun moves from one zodiacal constellation into the next one in about one month. Visualize this in Figure 1.

II. The Daily Motion of the Sun

As was demonstrated in Exercises 5.0 and 6.0:

Diurnal motion takes place along diurnal circles that are centered on the axis of rotation and are parallel to the celestial equator.

On the dates of the equinoxes, when the Sun's declination is 0°, its diurnal circle is coincident with the celestial equator. As seen from the north geographic pole, the Sun would be seen to circle the horizon in the course of the day and not rise or set. At all other latitudes the Sun rises at the east point and sets at the west point of the observer's horizon and there are equal lengths of daylight and darkness since the horizon cuts the celestial equator in half.

At the geographic pole, the celestial pole coincides with the zenith and the celestial equator coincides with the horizon.

On June 21 the declination of the Sun is +23.5°. At the north geographic pole the Sun circles parallel to the horizon at an altitude of 23.5° and does not set, resulting in 24 hours of continuous daylight. On December 21 the Sun's declination is -23.5° and the Sun is south of the celestial equator. At the north geographic pole on this date, the Sun moves around the observer in a circle parallel to the horizon but 23.5° below the horizon and does not rise.

In winter at mid-latitudes, the Sun rises south of east and sets south of west and the daytime is shorter than nighttime. In summer, when the Sun is north of the celestial equator, it rises north of east and sets north of west and there are more hours of daylight than darkness

At the north geographic pole, between March 21 and September 21, the Sun is above the horizon for 24 hours each day giving 6 months of continuous daylight. Between September 21 and March 21 the Sun's declination is negative and the Sun is below the horizon for 24 hours each day giving 6 months of continuous darkness. At the north geographic pole all objects with negative declinations remain below the horizon. Objects with positive declinations are circumpolar and have their diurnal circles entirely above the horizon. The reverse is true for the south geographic pole. In short, half of the sky is always visible and the other half is never visible at either geographic pole.

At the geographic equator, the celestial equator passes through the zenith and makes an angle of 90° with the horizon. The north and south celestial poles lie on the horizon. As seen from here, all objects rise and set vertically and there are no circumpolar objects. Every object is above the horizon for twelve hours and below it for twelve hours. The length of the daylight period is always twelve hours. The equator is also the only place where the Sun is at the zenith at noon on the dates of the equinoxes. The Sun can never be seen to pass overhead, through the zenith, at any latitude greater than 23.5°, in either hemisphere. The parallel of latitude 23.5° N. is sometimes called the Tropic of Cancer and its counterpart in the Southern Hemisphere is known as the Tropic of Capricorn.

III. Tutorial

Logon to **Skylab2** and select program No. 4, **Celestial Sphere**. From the Celestial Sphere menu, select **Animate Sun**. The computer will now draw an external view of the celestial sphere as seen from the latitude of TCNJ for the present date and time and then begin to animate both the

Exercise 7.0

diurnal and annual motion of the Sun. The diurnal motion can be seen as the motion of the Sun along its diurnal circle for whatever declination the Sun has today. The little cross on the celestial equator is the vernal equinox and one can simultaneously see the diurnal circle of this important point in the sky. The annual motion of the Sun shows up as the slow change in the Sun's declination from one day to the next and hence, a slight change in the Sun's diurnal circle from one day to the next. Pressing the space bar will stop the animation and a column of data will appear along the left margin of the screen. Do this. Among these data are the values for the right ascension and declination of the Sun and also its altitude and azimuth. Several different time readings will also appear but just pay attention to the **local apparent solar time (LAT). The local apparent solar time is defined to be the hour angle of the Sun plus 12 hours.** This time may differ by several minutes from the time on our clocks or **zone time (ZT)**. The reason for this difference is explained in Exercise 8.

Now press the space bar again to restart the motion. Allow the animation to run through the year and watch the changing declination of the Sun result in a different diurnal circle from one day to the next. You can speed up this motion by changing the step size to one hour. Press the space bar occasionally to get a readout of the right ascension (RA) and declination (DEC) of the Sun. Pay attention to the changing places on the horizon where the Sun rises and sets as the seasons advance. Also note that the upper and lower transit points for the Sun change.

Now do the same thing for latitude 60° and also 20° in order to study the differences in the Sun's motion for different places on the Earth. You might try to experiment with other latitudes such as the equator and the pole.

Now press the Esc key until you are back at the Main Menu. From the Main Menu select the *Skymation* routine to investigation the motion of the Sun as seen on a rectangular chart of the sky. When the chart appears you will see a bunch of letters moving around on the chart. These letters represent the planets and the Sun. To identify which is which, open the Symbol window by pressing the letter S on the keyboard. Hit the "Esc" key to remove the window.

The animation you see is the orbital motion of the planets, including the Earth's. The Earth's motion, of course, shows up as the apparent motion of the Sun along the ecliptic. The Sun is identified as the object **H**, which stands for Helios, the ancient Greek God of the Sun.

NOTE WELL: The position of the Earth cannot be shown on this chart, for that would be a contradiction. You must realize that your eyes are on the Earth, off the monitor screen. That is, the chart on the screen is a compressed view of the entire sky or celestial sphere around you and the Earth. It may help to try and associate what you see on the computer screen with what you see in the planetarium.

Now find the wavy red curve. This is the ecliptic, the annual path of the Sun around the celestial sphere. The points where this curve crosses the celestial equator are the equinoxes.
The vernal equinox is at right ascension RA = 0:00 and the autumnal equinox is at RA = 12:00.

The default step is one day. That is, the sky is being represented for the same time on successive days. If you want things to go faster or slower, change the step size as usual. Allow things to run and concentrate your attention on the Sun. Pay attention to the changing right ascension (RA) and declination (DEC) of the Sun. Remember it is the changing declination of the Sun that causes its diurnal circle to change. If you want the stars shown also, you may obtain them from the options window. Find out in what constellation the Sun is located on your birthday. Is it the one you usually associate with your horoscope?

It is important to realize that the motions animated on the rectangular chart are what one sees from an Earth that is just a point in space. Therefore, what is seen on this chart is true for any observer and is independent of geographic position.

Now pay attention to the moving blue vertical line. This is your local celestial meridian (LCM). The motion of this line represents the rotation of the Earth. That is, for the same solar time from one day to the next, the position of the stars relative to your celestial meridian (LCM) changes by 1° or 4^m of time. We shall investigate this matter in another exercise.

IV. Assignment

Now return to the program *Celestial Sphere* and then select *Animate Sun*. Your first objective will be to determine the date and time the Sun arrives at each of the equinoxes and solstices for the current year. Start with the vernal equinox and work your way through the year. Remember that the Sun may arrive at the equinoxes and solstices anywhere between the 19th and 23rd of the month, so you will have to search over these intervals to find the exact date and time for these events. Use the values for the RA of the Sun listed in the table in section I as the criteria for determining when the Sun is at one of the desired points. The Sun can arrive at any of these points at any time of the day as long as the RA is exactly the value listed in the table. Do not use the declination as the criterion or you will get the wrong answers. Make sure you work to the same precision as in Exercise 5.0 and record your data in the same way on the answer pages.

As you find the dates for the Sun to arrive at the equinoxes and solstices, stay on each date and determine the local apparent time (LAT) the Sun rises, makes UT, sets, and makes LT. To do this, proceed exactly the same way you did in Exercise 5.0 and use the same criteria for determining when the Sun rises, etc. When recording angles such as altitude, do not use colons. Instead use the symbols for degrees and arcminutes. Colons are to be used only for recording time.

After you have all the above data in hand for latitude 40° N., select one of the other latitude options below and repeat the same determinations. However, it is not necessary to determine the dates and times for the Sun to arrive at the equinoxes and solstices, since they should be the same. You need only copy the dates and times you found for latitude 40° N. onto the answer page for the other latitude.

The last part of this exercise is to draw the diurnal circles of the Sun for the above dates on the blank celestial sphere diagrams provided, one for each latitude. The data you compiled in the tables on the two answer pages will help you draw these circles. Also, some of the data will be used to annotate the diurnal circles that you draw.

Now proceed to do the above by following the steps listed below:

1. Now type "D" to call down the DATE menu, set your start date to March 19, and press Enter.
2. Type "O" for the options window menu and set your step size to 4 minutes. Press Enter.
3. Set the delay interval to 0.3 seconds and press Enter
4. Allow the animation to run and every now and then press the space bar to stop the motion and note the right ascension of the Sun.

NOTE: Use the values for the RA of the Sun as the criteria for these events and not the declination. When the right ascension (RA) of the Sun is exactly $0^h\ 00^m\ 00^s$, the Sun is at the vernal equinox. Try to stop the motion at this exact time, but no more than 1^s in right ascension (RA) different from this. You will find that there is an indeterminacy of about plus or minus 7 minutes in the local apparent time (LAT) to accomplish this. **Note: 24:00 = 0:00.**

5. Record the date and the local apparent time (LAT) at which the event occurs on the worksheet.
6. Now that you know the date, run the diurnal motion of the Sun backwards or forwards to determine the hour angle, altitude, azimuth, and local apparent time (LAT) when the Sun rises, makes upper transit (UT), sets, and makes lower transit (LT) on that date. **Warning: Do not run the diurnal motion backwards and forwards past midnight when trying to find lower transit (LT) or the computer will get the date mixed up.** If this happens, you will have to reset the date and start over.
7. Record these values on the answer sheet, using the degree and arcminute symbols when writing angles, such as, 25° 15'. **Do not use colons.**

Exercise 7.0

8. Repeat for the summer solstice, the autumnal equinox, and the winter solstice, using the right ascension (RA) as your criterion. You should know what the right ascension of the Sun has to be for these events. (See the table in section I.)
9. Repeat the above for the vernal equinoxes and solstices at the same longitude, but at the other latitude assigned by your instructor. Record the results on the other answer page.
10. Use a different blank celestial sphere diagram to draw the diurnal circles of the Sun for these dates at each of the two latitudes, as outlined in the next section. After you have drawn the diurnal circles, write the values of the local apparent times the Sun rises, makes upper transit (UT), sets, and makes lower transit (LT) next to points where the Sun does these things

V. How to Draw a Diurnal Circle

1. First use a protractor and locate the positions of the celestial poles. The latter are to be placed on the local celestial meridian (LCM) using the latitude angle. Don't know what to do? Refer to Exercise 6, where the concepts for this were presented.
2. Now draw a line connecting the poles. This line should pass through the center of the celestial sphere. This is the axis of rotation of the celestial sphere. Label it as such.
3. Now use the protractor and the latitude angle to find the two points where the celestial equator intersects the celestial meridian (LCM). Again, refer to Exercise 6 if you have forgotten the connection. Label the point on the upper LCM as Σ and the point on the lower LCM as Σ'.

   Warning: If your protractor is larger than the drawing of the celestial sphere, you will need to make marks that are off the **LCM** to indicate any angle you measure. To find where these marks should be on the **LCM**, lay a ruler along your mark and the center of the celestial sphere, then make a mark where the ruler crosses the **LCM**. This mark then indicates the actual point of upper or lower transit.

4. Now draw the celestial equator as an ellipse passing through these two points and the **East** and **West** points. Make the half of the ellipse on the back of the celestial sphere to be a dashed curve. This is the diurnal circle of the Sun on the days of the equinoxes.
5. Indicate somewhere along the celestial equator that the declination is $0°$ and draw 2 short, bold arrows along the circle, one on the back and one on the front, indicating the direction of diurnal motion.
6. At this point, check your diagram with those from Exercise 6. They should look consistent.
7. Look up the declination of the Sun when it as at the summer solstice. Then use a protractor to find the points of upper transit (UT) and lower transit (LT) for the Sun on the **local celestial meridian** by measuring an angular distance from the celestial equator equal to the declination. Label these points as **SUT** and **SLT**.

   Remember to set the protractor to measure declination from the celestial equator and not the horizon.

8. Once the points of upper and lower transit have been properly located on the **LCM**, connect these two points with a faint pencil line.
9. Through the point where the above line intersects the north-south (**N-S**) line, draw another faint guideline parallel to the east-west (**E-W**) line from horizon to horizon. The two points where this last line touches the horizon are the points where the Sun rises and sets. Label them as **SSR** and **SSS**.

10. Now draw the diurnal circle of the Sun as an ellipse that passes through the upper transit point (SUT), lower transit point (SLT), and the rise and set points. Again make the back half of the curve a dashed line.
11. Indicate the declination of the Sun along this circle and draw 2 short, bold arrows along the circles, one on the back and one on the front, indicating the direction of diurnal motion.
12. Repeat the above to draw the diurnal circle of the Sun for the winter solstice, except now use the declination of the Sun when it is at the winder solstice. The angle is negative, so you are to measure south from the celestial equator to find the upper and lower transit points. Replace **S** with **W** for labeling the UT, LT, Rise, and Set points.
13. When the diurnal circles are completed, write the values of local apparent time (**LAT**) when the Sun rises, makes upper transit, etc., next to the corresponding points along the diurnal circle.
14. Repeat all of the above on the other blank celestial sphere diagram for the other latitude for which you collected data.

When you have completed drawing and annotating the diurnal circles of the Sun for the different latitudes, study these diagrams to see how different the path of the Sun in the sky is from season to season and latitude to latitude. Note also the difference in times when the Sun rises and sets. Relate the fraction of the diurnal circle above and below the horizon to the length of daylight and nighttime and how this varies from latitude to latitude. **These are important concepts on which you will be tested.**

CHANGING DIURNAL CIRCLES OF THE SUN
WORKSHEET

Latitude_____

Date of VE: _____ . Local Apparent Time (LAT): _____

Event	Hour Angle	Altitude	Azimuth	LAT
Sunrise				
UT				
Sunset				
LT				

Date of SS: _____ . Local Apparent Time (LAT): _____

Event	Hour Angle	Altitude	Azimuth	LAT
Sunrise				
UT				
Sunset				
LT				

Date of AE: _____ . Local Apparent Time (LAT): _____

Event	Hour Angle	Altitude	Azimuth	LAT
Sunrise				
UT				
Sunset				
LT				

Date of WS: _____ . Local Apparent Time (LAT): _____

Event	Hour Angle	Altitude	Azimuth	LAT
Sunrise				
UT				
Sunset				
LT				

CHANGING DIURNAL CIRCLES OF THE SUN
WORKSHEET

Latitude_____

Date of VE: _____ , Local Apparent Time (LAT): _____

Event	**Hour Angle**	Altitude	Azimuth	**LAT**
Sunrise				
UT				
Sunset				
LT				

Date of SS: _____ . Local Apparent Time (LAT): _____

Event	**Hour Angle**	Altitude	Azimuth	**LAT**
Sunrise				
UT				
Sunset				
LT				

Date of AE: _____ , Local Apparent Time (LAT): _____

Event	**Hour Angle**	Altitude	Azimuth	**LAT**
Sunrise				
UT				
Sunset				
LT				

Date of WS: _____ Local Apparent Time (LAT): _____

Event	**Hour Angle**	Altitude	Azimuth	**LAT**
Sunrise				
UT				
Sunset				
LT				

Diurnal Circles of the Sun
Answer Diagram

Latitude _____

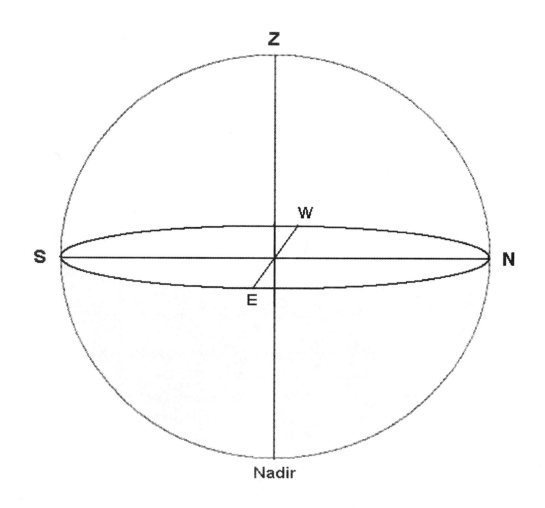

Diurnal Circles of the Sun
Answer Diagram

Latitude _____

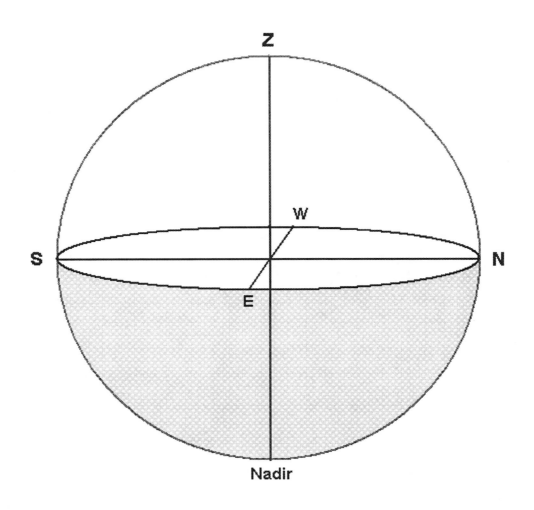

Exercise 7.2

THE MOTION OF THE SUN ALONG THE ECLIPTIC

I. Introduction

For an observer on the Earth, the Sun appears to move in a circle around the celestial sphere eastward with respect to the fixed stars. This circle is called the **ecliptic.** The ecliptic lies in the plane of the Earth's orbit. Thus the ecliptic is inclined to the celestial equator by 23.5°. This angle is referred to as the **obliquity of the ecliptic**. Therefore, as the Sun appears to move around the ecliptic over the course of a year, its angular distance from the celestial equator (declination) changes. The 2 points of intersection of the ecliptic and the celestial equator are called the **equinoxes**.

Now, the Earth takes 365.2422 days to complete a 360° orbit around the Sun. Therefore:

**In the sky, the Sun appears to move eastward along the ecliptic
about one degree per day, relative to the "fixed stars."**

This apparent motion of the Sun is merely a reflection of the Earth's revolution. On or about March 21, the Sun crosses the celestial equator moving from south to north. The Sun is then at the point called the vernal equinox. The Sun reaches its maximum northerly declination (+23.5°) on or about June 21. It is then at the point called the **summer solstice**. The point where the Sun is observed to cross the celestial equator as it moves from north to south is called the **autumnal equinox**. The point where the Sun reaches its maximum southerly declination (-23.5°) is the **winter solstice.**

II. Assignment

Run the program "Skymation."

1. Type "O" for options and plot the stars and then plot a grid.

2. Set the date to the one assigned to you by your instructor. The Time of day does not matter.

3. Obtain a printout of this chart.

4. Locate and label the equinoxes and solstices on the chart with the abbreviations VE, SS, AE, and WS.

5. On this chart, plot the position of the Sun where it will be twenty days later and label this point by what date that will be.

6. Locate the position of the Sun on November 15, using the method of interpolation as explained in class. Label this point by the date.

Exercise 7.5

SOLAR DIURNAL CIRCLES IN THE HORIZON SYSTEM

I. Introduction

In this exercise, we shall study how the diurnal circles of the Sun appear when viewed in a rectangular representation of the celestial sphere in the horizon system. There will be considerable distortion introduced by using a rectangular projection, so we shall limit the portion of the sky represented to just that seen when facing south. We shall see mainly the portion of the diurnal circle that is above the horizon.

II. Tutorial

Log on to **Skylab2** and select program No. 2, *Skymation*. A rectangular representation of the sky will now be displayed with animation of the motions of the Sun and planets in the equatorial system. Type "C" to open the coordinates menu. In this menu select *Horizon*.

Now type "P" for pan. Select "pan up" and press enter. Now change the pan factor to 15 units and press enter.

Now type "z" for zoom. Select "zoom out" and press enter. Use the zoom out factor of 3.5X and press enter.

Now type "O" for options and set the step to exactly 30 minutes and press the enter key.

Type "O" again and select "grid" and press enter.

Type "O" a 3rd time and select "Trail". Press enter and select "Sun" and press enter again.

Do not plot the stars or "trail" will not work.

Now observer the chart on the monitor screen. The vertical line in the center at azimuth 180° is the **LCM**. This should be in agreement with your understanding of the horizon system. The animation taking place represents how diurnal motion appears in the horizon system. Diurnal circles appear as wavy curves. As the Sun traces out its diurnal circle from east to west notice how its altitude and azimuth change. When the Sun is at upper transit on the LCM, its altitude is a maximum. As the days go by, the Sun's declination is slowly changing and, hence, its diurnal circle will be slightly different from one day to the next. This causes the trailing of the Sun's diurnal circle to grow thicker.

For the months between October and February you can see where the Sun rises and sets on the horizon. Recall that the East point of the horizon is at azimuth 90°.

What is the azimuth of the West point of the horizon?

To see the points where the Sun rises and sets for the other months of the year, one has to zoom out more. You might like to try this.

After you have watched the Sun long enough to understand what you are seeing, try trailing the moon and then Saturn. Can you explain the differences in the daily variations of the diurnal circles for these objects?

III. Assignment

1. Remove all trails by selecting trail again. Remain in the horizon system that you have been investigating and set the date to that which you determined in Ex.7.0 for the VE and the time to 0:00.

2. Now set to trail the Sun and allow it to move so that its diurnal circle is visible all the way across the screen and quickly stop the motion.

3. Now do the same for the day of the summer solstice and the winter solstice. **Do not call for trail again or you will erase the one you just obtained.**

4. Lastly, trail the Sun for your birthday. By doing your birthday last, the date at the top of the chart will be that one. If your birthday is within 20 days of one of the other dates, select some other date other than your birthday. Otherwise, you will not be able to distinguish the two separate diurnal circles.

You should now have four different diurnal circles of the Sun on your screen. Get a printout of this screen, showing all four diurnal circles of the Sun on one chart. By doing your birthday last, this date will be the one that comes out on your printout and you can readily identify your chart from anyone else's chart. Take your chart and do the following:

5. Write along the trail of each diurnal circle its date followed by "**DC Sun/Summer Solstice/Equinox/Winter Solstice**", as is appropriate. Actually, the diurnal circles for the vernal and autumnal equinoxes should be indistinguishable.

6. Identify the east, west, and south points of the horizon and label as E, W, and S. These notations should be just under the points to which they refer on the horizon. Note: The bottom of the chart is not the horizon!

7. Make eye estimates of the altitude and azimuth of the Sun at the points where it rises, sets, and makes upper transit for each of the four trails and write these values in a box near the point they represent. Your chart should look similar to the one shown to the right, except the example has only one diurnal circle, altitude and azimuth are listed only for upper transit, and the labeling of the diurnal circle is written horizontally rather than along the diurnal circle. Make sure you have done all these things before submitting your chart for review or grading.

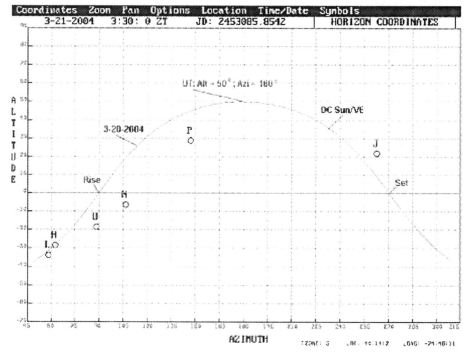

Exercise 8.0

HOUR ANGLES AND TIME

I. Time by the Sun

Time is the interval between two measurable events, such as the ticks of a clock or the beat of a heart. Before the invention of clocks, people often used the apparent motion of the Sun across the sky to tell time. Time using the visible or real Sun is called local apparent solar time and abbreviated as **LAT**. Local apparent solar time is defined to be the hour angle of the Sun ($HA_\odot$) plus twelve hours.

$$LAT = HA_\odot + 12:00$$

This is the time indicated on a sundial, that is, it is time by the position of the Sun in the sky relative to one's local celestial meridian. The event taking place here is the upper transit of the Sun. A long time ago it was decided that this interval should be called a day and that it consisted of exactly 24 hours.

However, LAT is not the time we use today on our clocks. There are two reasons for this. First, the real Sun moves at a varying rate along the ecliptic as a result of the Earth's variable speed in its elliptical orbit around the Sun. This means that the interval between upper transits of the Sun changes throughout the year. Secondly, the obliquity of the ecliptic also causes the length of the apparent solar day to be different at different times of the year. Hence, keeping time by the real Sun is not practical.

The time we use on our clocks is called zone time, **ZT**. Everyone living within a specified zone of longitudes agrees to use the same time on their clocks, regardless of the location of the Sun in the sky. This is necessary in a world where people travel relatively large distances very quickly. Zone time uses what is called the local mean solar time, **LMT**, of the central meridian of a time zone.

Everyone has a unique LMT that depends on their longitude. **LMT** is time kept by the position in the sky of a fictitious object called the **Mean (or average) Sun** that moves at a uniform rate around the celestial equator instead of the ecliptic.

LMT is the hour angle of the Mean Sun, as seen from a given longitude, plus 12 hours

Now we can define zonetime:

ZT is the hour angle of the Mean Sun, as seen from the central meridian of a time zone, plus 12 hours.

The amount that one's LMT differs from their zonetime depends on how far you are from the central meridian of your time zone. For the Eastern Time Zone, the central meridian is 75° W. of the prime meridian at Greenwich, England. If you are located east of a central meridian, such as Boston is in the Eastern Time Zone, your LMT is ahead or later than the zone time by several minutes. On the other hand, if you live in Detroit, which is also in the Eastern Time Zone but west of the central meridian, your LMT is about 22 minutes behind or earlier than EST. TCNJ is located about 0.25 degrees to the east of the central meridian of the Eastern Time Zone. Hence, EST is 1 minute earlier than the LMT at TCNJ.

Most astronomical handbooks and almanacs list celestial events for the Greenwich Mean Time, GMT, at which they occur. Greenwich Mean Time is also called Universal Time. To convert GMT to one's ZT, one adds the zone correction number which is -5^h for the eastern standard time zone, or -6^h for the central time zone, etc.

The amount that one's LMT differs from one's LAT depends on the time of the year. That is, sometimes the Mean Sun is ahead of the real Sun and sometimes it is behind the real Sun, depending on the real Sun's declination and how fast the Earth is moving in its orbit. The LAT minus the LMT is a number that is called the Equation of Time and abbreviated as **ET**.

$$ET = LAT - LMT$$

This is a number that expresses how much the mean Sun is ahead or behind the real Sun. That is, ET is a number that is algebraically added to the LMT to get the LAT. The possible values for ET range from $+17^m$ to -14^m.

Because we use zonetime or LMT rather than LAT on our clocks, the earliest sunset occurs about December 8 rather than the day of the winter solstice. See if you can notice this in December. Similarly, the latest sunrise is on January 5 rather than the day of the winter solstice. There is a similar effect for sunrise and sunset near the summer solstice.

II. Sidereal Time

Astronomer's use another kind of time called Sidereal Time. One's local sidereal time, or **LST**, is defined as the western (+) hour angle of the vernal equinox, that is, the time elapsed since the last upper transit of the VE. Therefore, it can never be a negative number.

$$LST = + HA_{VE}$$

The local sidereal time (LST) is also the right ascension of any object making upper transit. Sidereal time is time by the stars rather than by the sun. A clock that keeps sidereal time is used by astronomers to locate objects with a telescope. A useful relation between the LST and the RA and HA for any object (star, Moon, or planet) is:

$$LST = RA + HA$$

We shall make use of this equation in Ex. 9.

Since the real and mean suns have a motion of about $1°$ per day eastward with respect to the fixed stars, the solar day is longer than the sidereal day by about 4 minutes of sidereal time. This is caused by the revolution of the Earth in its orbit.

There are 24 hours of solar time in a solar day and 24 hours of sidereal time in a sidereal day. Hence the two kinds of hours are not the same length. The sidereal hours are slightly shorter than the solar hours. This means the sidereal clock runs faster than the solar clock. However, the sidereal clock keeps track of the true rotation of the Earth on its axis, that is, the time for the Earth to rotate through $360°$. Remember, the length of the solar day is complicated by the revolution of the Earth.

The sidereal clock and the solar clock agree on one day of the year and that is the day of the autumnal equinox. Thereafter, the sidereal clock gains 4 minutes per day on the solar clock.

III. Tutorial

Logon to **SKYLAB2** and select program No. 2, Skymation. After you press the Enter key, a rectangular representation of the celestial sphere will appear on the monitor screen with an animation of the day to day changes in the positions of the nine major planets, the Sun, and the Moon. The latter are identified by code letters, which can be interpreted by means of a drop-down "Symbols" table. To see this table, type "S". Press Esc to remove this window.

Now type "O" to bring down the options menu. Select "grid" to be plotted and then select "Plot Stars". Now watch the animation and note the following: The zone time, ZT, and the date are displayed in a band at the top of the chart. The eastwardly moving, vertical line is the local celestial meridian, LCM. The hour circle of right ascension coincident with the LCM at any instant indicates the local sidereal time, LST. Remember that the LST is also the hour angle of the VE. On the screen or rectangular star chart, the hour angle of any object is the horizontal distance E/W from the LCM at any instant, that is, it is the distance measured parallel to the parallels of declination.

The positions of the LCM and the planets on the chart are shown initially for the date and zone time that you start the program and they jump to their positions for successive one day or 24 hour intervals thereafter. Notice that the date changes by one day intervals but the zone time remains the same. The step size and delay factor can be changed from the Options window. The initial time and date to begin the animation can be changed from the Time/Date window.

Notice that as the days progress, the sidereal time (the RA circle coincident with the LCM) increases by four minutes, for the same zone time. Can you explain this?

Now set the step size to 10 minutes and the delay factor to 0.5 seconds and allow the animation to run. Diurnal motion now is represented by the changing position of the LCM, which moves opposite to the direction of the rotating celestial sphere. Now, instead of showing the stars and planets moving along their diurnal circles from east to west past the LCM, the stars are fixed and the LCM moves west to east. But upper transit is still when the object crosses the LCM.

Note that as the LCM moves over the course of a day, the planets change their positions relative to the stars by very little, except for one object. Which object noticeably changes its RA and DEC from hour to hour? The motions of the planets relative to the stars are a result of their orbital motions in the solar system. As the days go by you can notice the position of the Sun changing. Notice how it stays on the ecliptic and moves eastward by about one degree per day. What causes this motion?

Occasionally stop the animation by pressing the space bar. Notice the distance between the Sun and the LCM in time units, with minus for east and positive for west. If you add twelve to this, you get the local apparent time by the Sun, **LAT**. It should be a number that is close to the zone time. In fact, the difference between the two is the equation of time, **ET**. (If you didn't follow this, go back to the section on the difference between LAT, ZT, and LMT and reread it again.) Now try stopping the animation on different dates and at different times and repeat this measurement and make estimations of the ET.

Now we shall demonstrate the difference between LMT and LAT in another way. Type C to open the coordinates window and select "Horizon." Now an animation of the sky is shown facing south in the horizon system. Your LCM is the stationary red vertical line in the middle of the screen at azimuth 180°. Other values of azimuth are along the horizontal axis and altitude is along the vertical axis.

Type Z to zoom out and do so by the factor of 2 that appears as the default value. Under Options, set the step size to 5 days and the Time (which is the zone time and practically the same as your local mean time) to 12:00. Now make 3 separate selections under Options: (1) **Grid**, (2) **Remove Stars**, and then (3) **Trail**. You will need to make each of these as separate selections, pressing Enter after each one. When you press Enter after selecting "Trail," another window will open to allow you to select which object you wish to trail. Select "Sun" and press Enter until the skymation chart returns. The Trail function will not work unless you nave removed the stars.

Now watch the animation run through the year. Remember we are viewing the sky every 5 days at LMT=noon and the Sun will leave a trail showing how sometimes it is ahead of the LMT and sometimes it is behind. The Sun will form a pattern that looks like a figure 8. This is called the **analemma**. As you watch the Sun trace out the pattern of the analemma, try to relate the changing altitude of the Sun with the changing diurnal circles of the sun that were studied in exercise 7.0. When the analemma is completed, follow the instructions for obtaining a hardcopy of the screen image.

The analemma is a graphical representation of the equation of time. The horizontal distance from the LCM to any point on the analemma is the value of the equation of time, ET, for a particular day of the year. The analemma is sometimes shown on a globe of the Earth for the purpose of determining the equation of time.

III. Assignment

Return to the equatorial coordinates chart for Skymation. Now type "T" to bring down the Time\Date window. Set the zone time (ZT) and then the date to a value a few days before the one assigned to you. **Do not select a zone time near 12:00 noon.** Under "options" set the step size back to 1 day and delay time to 0.70 seconds.

Now let the animation run and stop it at the date and time assigned to you. Obtain a printout of the screen. When you get your chart, proceed to analyze it as follows, **making all measurements with a precision of 2 decimal places and recording as such:**

1. Measure the distance along the bottom of the chart in centimeters from 0.00 hours of RA to 24.00 hours. Record your answer on the answer sheet, making sure you have 2 numbers after the decimal point, even if they are zeros.
2. Divide the 24.00 hours by the number of centimeters that you measured in step 1. The result is the right ascension chart scale in hours per centimeter. Record this on the answer sheet with 4 significant figures.
3. Locate the upper meridian and label it as **ULCM** near the top of the chart. Then find where the upper meridian intersects the right ascension scale and try to read this value by eye with a precision of plus or minus 2 minutes of RA. Do not read the RA with a decimal part. This value is the local sidereal time, LST. Record your answer on the answer page like this: **5:09**.
4. Locate the vernal equinox and measure the horizontal distance in cm from the upper LCM to the VE. This measurement is the hour angle of the VE in cm. Record this on the answer page indicating that it is a western hour angle.
5. Multiply the above value by the chart scale from No. 2 to convert cm to hours and decimal parts thereof. Record your result on the answer page and label as W.
6. Take the decimal part of the above answer and multiply by 60 minutes/hour to convert this decimal part of an hour to minutes. Now write the hours and minutes on the answer page like this: $8^h 52^m$ **W**. This is the western hour angle of the VE in hours and minutes. Allowing an error in your measurement of a few minutes, this answer should agree with the one from No. 3. That is, the local sidereal time is the western hour angle of the VE, or the right ascension of an object on the upper meridian (making upper transit).

Take note of the procedure in 5 and 6 for converting a measurement in cm to hours and minutes of RA, hour angle, or time. You will use this procedure below.

7. Draw a dashed vertical line through the Sun from the top of the chart to the bottom. This is the hour circle of RA of the Sun. Now draw a horizontal line from the upper LCM to the center of the circle representing the Sun with an arrowhead at the Sun. Measure the length of this line in cm with 2 decimal places and record on the answer page as the hour angle of the Sun in cm. Also label whether it is east or west.
8. Convert the above measurement to hours and minutes using the procedure in 5 and 6 and record on the answer page as the hour angle of the Sun. Also indicate direction east or west.
9. Use the relation LAT = $HA_{\odot}$ + 12:00 and the above value to compute the local apparent time. Record the result on the answer page.

Exercise 8.0 Continued

10. Draw a vertical line through Saturn from the top of the chart to the bottom. This is the hour circle of RA passing through Saturn. Try to read the RA of Saturn by eye with a precision of plus or minus 2 minutes. Do not read the RA in hours and decimal parts thereof but in hours and minutes and record on the answer sheet like this: $22^h\ 03^m$.

11. Draw a horizontal line from the upper LCM to Saturn with an arrowhead at Saturn. Be sure this line is drawn clearly separated from any other horizontal line that you have drawn. Measure the length of this line in cm to the hundredth place and record on the answer page as the hour angle of Saturn in cm east or west.

12. Use the above procedure for converting hour angle in cm to hour angle in hours and minutes east or west and record on the answer page.

13. Use the relation LST = RA + HA and the RA and HA values you found for Saturn and calculate the local sidereal time, LST. Don't forget to use the proper algebraic sign with the HA. Record the result on the answer page. Your answer should reasonably agree with the value you found for LST in either step 3 or 6.

14. Draw a horizontal line from the upper LCM to the Moon with an arrowhead at the Moon. Measure this distance in cm and record on the answer page as the hour angle of Moon in cm east or west.

15. Use the chart scale to compute the hour angle of the Moon in decimal hours east or west and then convert to hours and minutes east or west.

16. Use the answer to No. 15 to determine at what ZT the Moon will make UT or at what ZT it did make UT (whichever occurred most recently relative to the ZT at the top of the chart)?

17. List all the objects (Sun, Moon, and planets) that are within 6 hours east or west of the upper LCM.

18. Draw a dashed, vertical line from the top to the bottom of the chart at a distance of exactly 12 hours of RA from the upper LCM. Clearly label this line as the lower LCM. If the LST is less than 12:00, the lower LCM should be to the left of the upper LCM on the chart. If the LST is greater than 12:00, the lower LCM should be to the right of the upper LCM.

19. Record the RA aligned along the lower LCM in hours and minutes on the answer page.

20. List all the objects that are within 6 hours east or west of the lower LCM. These objects are closer to lower transit than to upper transit.

Exercise 8.0 Answer Page

Time and Hour Angles

01. Measured distance from 0^h to 24^h : _____ cm = 24.00 hours

02. Chart scale for converting cm to hours: _____ hrs./cm

03. RA aligned along the upper LCM in hours and minutes (LST): _____

04. Measured western hour angle of VE in centimeters: _____ cm

05. Hour angle of VE in hours and decimal parts thereof: _____ hours

06. Hour angle of VE in hours and minutes of time (LST); _____

07. Measured hour angle of the Sun in centimeters E/W: _____ cm

08a. Hour angle of the Sun in decimal hours E/W: _____ hours

08b. Hour angle of the Sun in hours and minutes E/W: _____

09   Computed value for LAT in hours and minutes, e. g. 14:22: _____
     Show calculation here:

10. Eye reading of Saturn's RA in hours and minutes: _____

11. Measured hour angle of Saturn in centimeters: _____ cm

12a. Hour angle of Saturn in decimal hours: _____ hours

12b. Hour angle of Saturn in hours and minutes east or west: _____

13. Calculated value of LST from RA and HA of Saturn, e. g. 14:22: _____
     Show calculation here:

14. Measured hour angle of the Moon in cm east or west: _____ cm

15. Hour angle of the Moon in decimal hours: _____ and in hours and minutes _____ .

17. Computed ZT for upper transit of the Moon in hours and minutes, e. g. 14:22: _____ .

18. Objects within 6 hours of upper transit: _____

     _____

19. RA aligned along lower LCM in hours and minutes: _____

20. Objects within 6 hours of lower transit: _____

     _____

Exercise 8.5

DETERMINING THE EQUATION OF TIME

I. Introduction

In Exercise 8.0, it was learned that the amount that one's local mean time, LMT, differs from one's local apparent solar time, LAT, depends on the time of the year. That is, sometimes the Mean Sun is ahead of the Real Sun and sometimes it lags behind (is farther to the east). This depends on the Real Sun's declination and on how fast the Earth is moving in its orbit around the Sun.

The LAT minus the LMT us a number that is called the Equation of Time, ET:

$$ET = LAT - LMT$$

The value of ET expresses how much the Mean Sun is ahead or behind the Real Sun. That is, ET is a number that is algebraically added to the local mean time to find the local apparent time. The value for ET can never be outside the range from +17 minutes to –14 minutes.

Because we use LMT rather than LAT on our clocks, the earliest sunset occurs on December 8 rather than on the day of the winter solstice and the latest sunrise occurs on January 5. There is a similar effect in summer with the latest sunset on June 28 and earliest sunrise on June 15.

II. Tutorial

Logon to **Skylab2** and select the program No. 2, **Skymation**. After you press the enter key, a rectangular representation of the celestial sphere will appear on the monitor screen with an animation of the day to day changes in the positions of the nine major planets, the Sun, and the Moon. The latter may be identified by code letters, which may be interpreted by a drop-down "Symbols" table. To see this table, type the letter "S." To remove the table, press the Esc key.

Now type the letter "O" to open the "Options" menu. Select "Grid" to be plotted and then select "Plot Stars". Now watch the animation. As the days go by, note that the zonetime stays the same. This is because the default step size is exactly 24 hours. Occasionally stop the animation by pressing the space bar. Notice the distance between the Sun and the LCM in time units, minus for east and positive for west. This is the hour angle of the Sun. if you add twelve hours to this, you get the LAT. It should be a number that is close to the zonetime.

The zonetime differs from your LMT by an amount of time equivalent to the difference between your longitude and the longitude of the central meridian of your time zone. For TCNJ, the LMT is one minute greater than the Eastern Standard Time. So, to find the LMT at TCNJ, add one minute to the zonetime. Once you know your LMT, the value of ET is given by the equation from section I, viz., ET = LAT - LMT.

Repeat your estimation of the LAT and ET for widely different dates of the year and at different times until you see how the value of ET changes.

III. Assignment

Type C to open the coordinates window and select 'Horizon." Now an animation of the sky is shown facing south in the horizon system. Your LCM is the stationary red vertical line in the middle of the screen at azimuth 180°. Other values of azimuth are along the horizontal axis and altitude is along the vertical axis.

Type Z to zoom out and do so by the factor of 2 that is offered for the default value. Under Options, set the step size to 5 days and the Time (which is the zonetime) to 12:00 (noon). Now under

"Options", select "Grid" and press "Enter". Then "Options" again and highlight "Trail". When you press "Enter", another window will open to allow you to select which object you wish to trail. Select "Sun" and press "Enter" until the "Skymation" chart returns. Now watch the animation run through the year. Remember, you are viewing the sky every 5 days at LMT = 12:00 (noon). Therefore, the Sun will leave a trail showing how sometimes it is ahead of the LMT and sometimes it is behind. The Sun will form a pattern that looks like a figure 8. This is called the **analemma.**

As you watch the Sun trace out the pattern of the analemma, try to relate the changing altitude of the Sun with the changing diurnal circles of the Sun that were studied in Exercise 7.0. When the analemma is completed, obtain a hardcopy. Label this printout #1.

The analemma is a graphical representation of the equation of time. The horizontal distance from the LCM to any point on the analemma is the value of the equation of time, ET, for a particular day of the year. The analemma is sometimes shown on a globe of the Earth for the purpose of determining the equation of time.

Just for fun, you might try trailing the planet Mercury. Why does Mercury display the pattern that you see? The answer depends on the size of Mercury's orbit compared with the Earth's orbit.

Return to the equatorial-coordinates chart for Skymation. Now type "T" to bring down the Time\Date window. Set the date to September 20, for the current year, at the zonetime (ZT) given to you by your instructor or 13:00. Set the step size back to 1 day and delay time to a convenient value to do the following assignment.

Allow the animation to run and stop It on September 25. Now get printout #2. Repeat and get printouts for Nov. 3 (#3) and Jan. 10 (#4) at the same zonetime (13:00). After you have all three charts, proceed to analyze them as follows:

1. Determine the RA chart scale for the 3 charts, following steps 1 and 2 in section **III** of Exercise 8.0. You need do this for only one of the charts. Write the appropriate results on the answer sheet.

2. Enter the zonetime from each chart in the first column of the answer sheet. Then determine the local mean time from the zonetime as explained in section **II**. Enter these values in the 2nd column.

3. Draw a horizontal line from the upper LCM to the center of the Sun on each chart. The length of this line is the hour angle of the Sun.

4. Measure the hour angle of the Sun to the nearest hundredth of a cm for each of the three days. Measure from the LCM, east or west, to the center of the little circle that represents the Sun. Remember that the equation of time is just a few minutes, so you have to measure very carefully. Write these values on the printout along the line representing the hour angle and label them to be the hour angle of the Sun. See the example chart at the end of this exercise. Also record this measurement in column 4 on the answer sheet.

5. Now use the chart scale found in step 1 and convert the measurements in column 4 to decimal hours.

6. Now convert the decimal hours to hours and minutes and record in column 5. Remember to indicate whether the angle is E or W. Next, compute the local apparent time, LAT. To do this, remember how LAT is defined in terms of the hour angle of the real Sun. Record the results on the answer sheet in column 6.

7. Lastly, compute the value of the equation of time, ET, for each of the three days and enter the results in the last column. Take care to get the correct algebraic sign on ET.

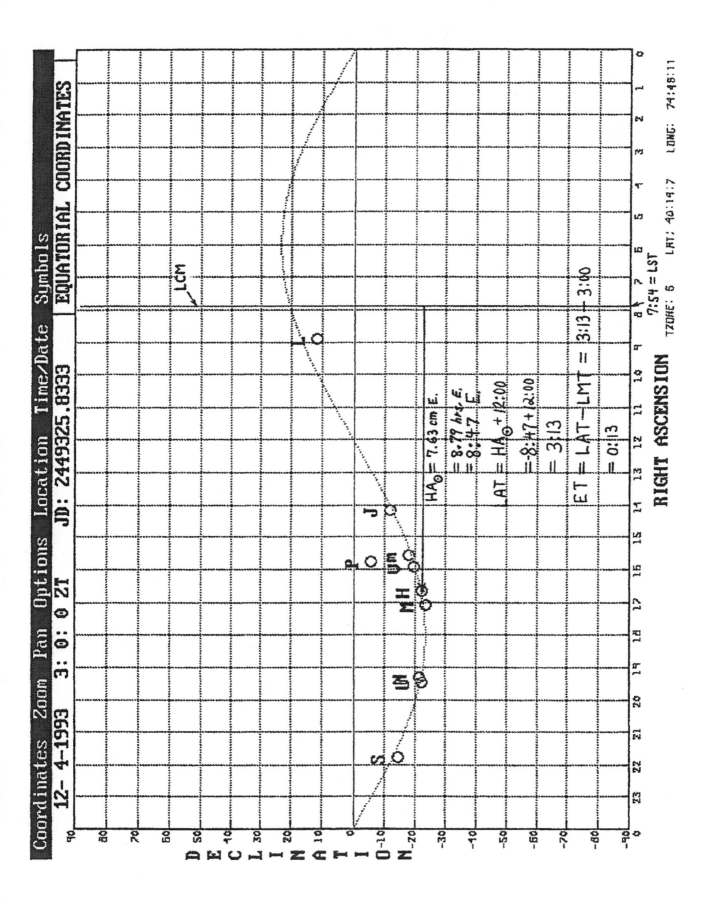

EQUATION OF TIME
WORK AND ANSWER SHEET

Determination of Chart Scale:

1. Distance from VE to 24th hour circle of RA: _____cm.

2. Chart scale (divide hours by cm) _____hr/cm.

Use the above chart scale to convert the hour angle of the real Sun in centimeters (column 4 below) to the hour angle in hours and decimal parts thereof. Then convert the decimal part of the hours into minutes and record below in column 5, using the format indicated.

Determination of Some Values for the Equation of Time (ET):

Date	ZT	LMT	HA$_\odot$(cm)	HA$_\odot$(hh:mm)	LAT	ET(0:mm)

Exercise 9.0

POSITIONS AND HOUR ANGLES

Equipment Needed: A Celestial Globe

This exercise assumes you have some familiarity with the Celestial Equatorial System of coordinates and the meaning of **right ascension (RA), hour angle (HA), and sidereal time (ST)**. Examine the globe and find the **celestial equator.** Now find the **vernal equinox** and the hour circle passing through it (the equinoctial colure.) If these terms are not familiar to you, you should review them before continuing with this exercise. Recall that right ascension is measured eastward from the vernal equinox (or equinoctial colure) and declination is measured north and south of the celestial equator.

Now locate and identify on the globe the following objects and their constellations. Most stars in the same constellation are connected by lines, but not all. Constellations are indicated by names with all upper case letters. Individual stars are labeled with names that have lower case letters, except the first. Star clusters, galaxies, and nebulae are indicated by asterisks labeled with numbers from Messier's Catalog, e.g., M57.

	RA	DEC	Object	Constellation
1.	4:36	+16:29	_____	_____
2.	5:15	-08:12	_____	_____
3.	20:42	+45:18	_____	_____
4.	16:27	-26:15	_____	_____

The globe will now be used to visualize and determine the hour angles for certain objects. To do this, count the number of hours and minutes from the local celestial meridian (**LCM**) along the celestial equator to the hour circle of the object in question. Use the RA scale to assist you. **Measure the hour angle (HA) eastward or westward, depending on which is the shorter distance.** You can verify your results by means of the following relationship, which is valid for any celestial object:

$$HA = LST - RA.$$

The diagram at the end of this exercise may be helpful to visualize this relation. Remember that the sidereal time is the hour circle of RA that is coincident with the LCM. When finding the sidereal time for the following questions, just read the right ascension aligned along the **LCM**.

Recall from Exercise 6.0 that the *altitude of the pole is equal to the latitude of the observer*, and that at upper transit (UT), an object is on the celestial meridian (**LCM**). Also recall from above that the numbers inscribed on the metallic celestial meridian of the globe are *declinations, not altitudes*

Now set the globe for latitude for 40° N, then set the Vernal Equinox at upper transit. Now answer the following, referring to paragraph 3 above on how to determine hour angle and sidereal time.

Exercise 9.0

     5. What is the sidereal time? ...._____.

     6. What is the hour angle (E/W) for object No. 1? ...._____

     7. What is the hour angle (E/W) for object No. 4? ...._____

For the following set the 6th hour circle of right ascension (RA) on the local celestial meridian (LCM):

     8. What is the sidereal time? ...._____

     9. What is the hour angle of Object No.1? ...._____

     10. What is the hour angle of Object No. 4? ...._____

Check that the globe is still set for latitude 40° N for the following events:

     11. What is the hour angle (HA) of Object No.1 when it rises? ...... _____

     12. What is the hour angle (HA) of Object No. 2 when it rises? ...... _____

     13. What is the hour angle (HA) of Object No. 4 when it rises? .... _____

    Now locate the **ecliptic** on the globe. The Sun's position along the ecliptic is marked for each day of the year and a date is written every 5 days. Turn the knob near the NCP to position the Sun where it would be on October 15. (Make sure the globe is set for latitude 40° N)

     14. In what constellation is the Sun located? _____

     15. What is the sidereal time when the Sun is at upper transit (UT)? _____

     16. What is the altitude of the Sun when it is at upper transit (UT)? _____

     17. What is the sidereal time when the Sun is at lower transit (LT)? _____

     18. Rotate the globe so the Sun is at lower transit (LT). Now identify the constellations that are at upper transit (UT) for the following declinations:

          A. Dec. = -30° _____

          B. Dec =- -15° _____

          C. Dec = +45° _____

          D. Dec = +65° _____

Set the Sun on the globe for its position on June 15 at latitude 40° N.

     19. In what constellation is the Sun located? .... _____

     20. What is the sidereal time when the Sun is at upper transit (UT) on 6/15? _____

21. What is the altitude of the Sun when it is at upper transit (UT) on 6/15? _____

22. Rotate the globe so the Sun is at lower transit (LT). Now identify the constellations at upper transit (UT) for the following declinations:

    A. Dec = -30° _____

    B. Dec = 0° _____

    C. Dec = +30° _____

    D. Dec = +70° _____

Set the Sun on the globe at its position for March 21 at latitude 40° N.

23. In what constellation is the Sun located? _____

24. Rotate the globe so the Sun is setting.

    A. What is the sidereal time? _____

    B. List the constellations that are above the horizon and near upper transit

      1. _____   2. _____

      3. _____   4. _____

      5. _____   6. _____

25. Rotate the globe so the Sun is at lower transit.

    A. What is the sidereal time? …………………………… _____

    B. Again, list the constellations that are above the horizon and near upper transit:

      1. _____   2. _____

      3. _____   4. _____

      5. _____   6. _____

The diagram below depicts the celestial sphere as seen by an observer when their local sidereal time is 4:40. Circles and angles are drawn and labeled in an attempt to show the relationships among right ascension (α), hour angle (**HA**), and local sidereal time (**LST**). Some very important relationships are:

1. **All objects with the same right ascension have the same hour angle at any given time.**

2. **All objects with the same right ascension make upper transit at the same time.**

3. **The local sidereal time is the right ascension of all objects at upper transit.**

Exercise 9.0

4. **All objects with the same right ascension do not rise or set at the same time, because this also depends on the declination of an object.**

In the diagram below, an hour circle is drawn connecting all objects with a right ascension of 7^h 50^m. Note that they all have an hour angle of -3^h 10^m at local sidereal time of 4:40, in agreement with the relation:

$$HA = LST - RA$$

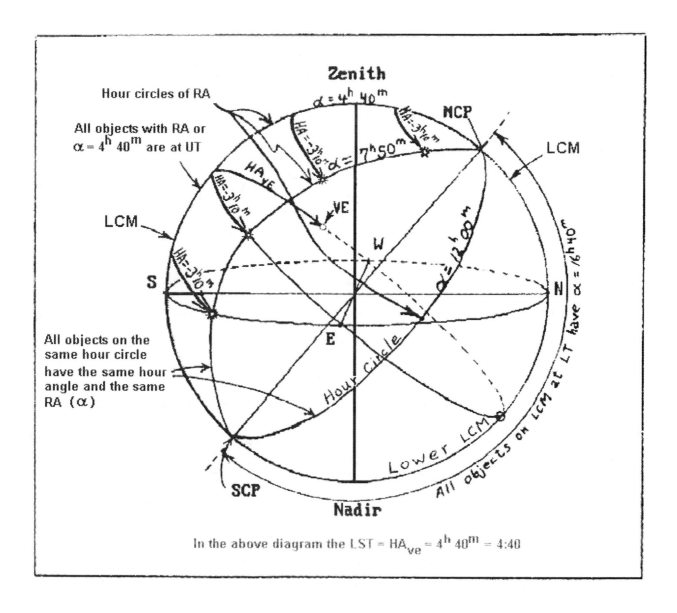

Exercise 10.0

LOCATING PLANETS, STARS AND CONSTELLATIONS IN THE SKY

I. Introduction

In this exercise, you will learn a way of locating objects in the sky on any day, at any time, and in any year. It is assumed you are familiar with both the Celestial Equatorial System of coordinates and the Horizon System. Also, you should know where the cardinal points of the compass are located on the horizon for the site where you will make your observations and, thereby, be able to visualize how your local celestial meridian (**LCM**) arcs across the sky.

II. Procedure

1. Logon to SKYLAB2 and go to the program Skymation.
2. Use the options window to plot the stars and draw a grid.
3. Set the time, date and year to correspond to when you will be doing your observations or use the time and date given to you by your instructor. Then get a printout of this chart and do the following analysis. Alternatively, your instructor may give you a chart to analyze.

The chart shows where the Sun, Moon, planets, and most of the visible stars are located relative to your **LCM**. Recall that what is shown on the chart is actually the half of the **LCM** where upper transit occurs and, therefore, it is called the upper local celestial meridian, **ULCM**. Also recall that the position of the **ULCM** along the RA scale indicates the sidereal time.

4. Label the **ULCM** on your chart.
5. Measure along the top boundary line of the chart, a distance equivalent to 6 hours of RA to the left (east) of the ULCM and mark this point.
6. Now do the same along the bottom boundary line and then connect these two points with a vertical line. See the example chart on the last page of this exercise.
7. Find the point where this line crosses the celestial equator (CE) and label this point as **E**. This point indicates what objects will be rising near the East Point of the horizon, for the time and date you have selected.
8. Now proceed as above and draw a vertical line at a distance 6 hours of RA to the right (west) of the ULCM.
9. Find the point where this vertical line intersects the CE and label as **W**. Now you will be able to identify what objects will be setting near the West Point of the horizon.
10. Now mark the point where the ULCM intersects the parallel of declination given by: $\delta =$ latitude $- 90°$. This is the South Point of the horizon; label this point **S**.
11. Now draw a curve, to look like a shallow bowl, connecting the **E**, **S**, and **W** points of the horizon that you have just located. This curve may run off one side of the chart. If so, you have to imagine it continues back on the chart at the other side. This curve indicates the location of the southern horizon. It enables you to see which stars of negative declination are above or below the horizon, at the time you have selected, and how far they are from upper transit.
12. To find the Zenith, find where the ULCM intersects the parallel of declination that is equal to your latitude. Mark this point as **Z**.
13. Now proceed as follows to find the other half of the horizon: As above, measure a distance

Exercise 10.0

equivalent to 12 hours of RA either to the east or west of the LCM along the top and bottom of the chart. Mark these points and then connect them with a vertical line. This line is the lower half of the LCM. Label it as **LLCM**. Objects near this line are making lower transit.

14. Find where the **LLCM** intersects the parallel of declination equal to $\delta = 90° -$ (your latitude). (This would be at $\delta = +50°$ for latitude 40° N.) This point locates the North Point of the horizon, so label it **N**.

15. Now draw a curve, looking like an inverted shallow bowl, connecting the **E**, **N**, and **W** points of the horizon. This curve will be the northern half of the celestial horizon and it will now be possible to see which stars of positive declination are above or below the horizon and how far they are from the LCM.

Compare your chart with the one at the end of this exercise. What you have drawn should be consistent with what is shown on that chart.

As time goes by, imagine the horizon sliding to the left (eastward) on the chart relative to the stars. This is another way of visualizing diurnal motion on the chart. The E and W points will slide along the CE, the S point will slide along the parallel of declination –50° (for latitude 40° N), and the N point will slide along the parallel of declination +50°. Remember that the N and S celestial poles are the top and bottom boundaries of the chart.

If you have completed Ex. 2.5, compare this chart with that one, in order to identify what constellations are above the horizon or near the LCM. Take the chart outside with you at the time you selected and try to locate these constellations and any planets that should be visible. The following rules will help you locate the stars; **they are concepts you should have learned in Ex. 5 and 6.**

1. **The stars at the zenith will be those on the LCM at a declination equal to your latitude.**

2. **The stars that will be setting at the West Point will be those with a declination near 0° and six hours west of the LCM.**

3. **The stars rising at the East Point will be those with a declination near 0° but six hours east of the LCM.**

4. **Stars with a declination equal to your latitude minus 90° will be at the south point of the horizon. Hence it will not be possible to see these stars or any stars with a declination smaller than this value.**

5. **Stars with a declination greater than 90° minus your latitude will be circumpolar stars of perpetual apparition and can always be seen somewhere around their diurnal circles.**

III. Using the Chart

Once the horizon is located on a rectangular star chart, the chart may be used to determine when an object will rise or set. To do this, simply measure the distance of the object along its parallel of declination (its diurnal circle) to the horizon and use the RA chart scale to convert cm to decimal hours and then hours and minutes. Measuring the distance from the eastern horizon yields the amount of time until the object rises or how long ago it rose, depending on whether the object is east or west of the eastern horizon. Similarly, measuring the distance from the western horizon yields the amount of time until the object sets or how long ago it set. To determine the actual zone time (ZT) the star or planet will rise or set, add or subtract your result to the ZT given at the top of the chart. With these general concepts in mind, follow the directions on the answer page.

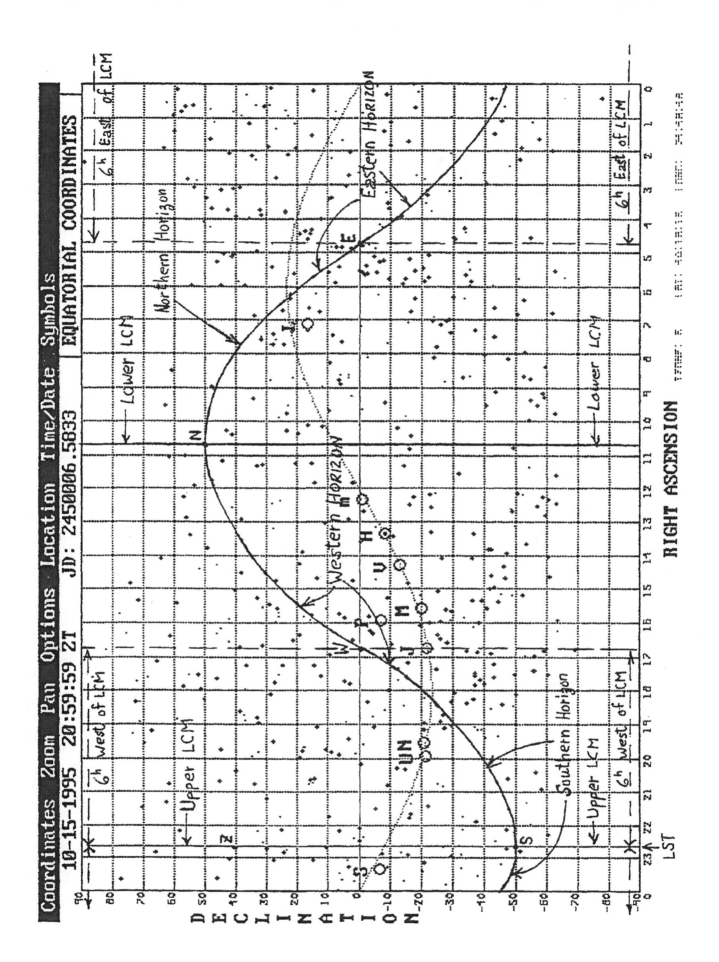

EXERCISE 10.0 ANSWER SHEET

1. Determine the right ascension chart scale for your chart following steps 1 and 2 of Exercise 8, and record the relevant data below:

   Measured distance in cm. (including 2 decimal places) from 0^h to 24^h : .... _____ (cm)

   RA chart scale (to 4 significant figures): .... _____ (hr/cm)

2. What is the sidereal time hours and minutes? .... _____

3. What is the hour angle of the Moon? .... _____ (cm) = _____ (hh:mm, E/W).

4. Is the Moon above or below the horizon? .... _____ .

5. How much time since or until the Moonrise, whichever is shorter?

   Distance from eastern horizon: _____ (cm) = Amount of time: _____ (hh:mm).

6. Subtract or add the above amount of time to the zone time to find Moonrise: _____ (hh:mm).

7. What is the hour angle of Venus? .... _____ (cm) = _____ (hh:mm E/W).

8. How much time since or until Venus sets, whichever is shorter?

   Distance from western horizon: _____ (cm) = Amount of time: _____ (hh:mm).

9. Add or subtract the above amount of time to find when Venus sets: _____ (hh:mm).

10. Alpha Orionis has RA=5:55 and Dec.=+8°. Measure its hour angle in cm and then use the chart scale to convert to time:

    Measured hour angle in cm: _____ (cm) = _____ (hr) = _____ (hh:mm E/W).

11. Is this star visible at the present time? .... _____ .

12. Which planet is closest to upper transit? .... _____ .

Exercise 11.0

PRECESSION OF THE EARTH'S AXIS

I. Introduction

The gravitational pull of the Sun and Moon on the Earth's equatorial bulge causes the Earth's axis of rotation to gyrate or precess in a cycle which takes about 26,000 years. However, this does not change the 23.5° tilt of the Earth's axis. As a result, the two points on the celestial sphere to which the Earth's axis points are changing relative to the fixed stars. By definition, these two moving points are the celestial poles. Hence, the NCP migrates in a circle of radius 23.5° around the north ecliptic pole once every 26,000 years. See the diagram below. This means that the present North Star, which is called Polaris, has not always been the North Star.

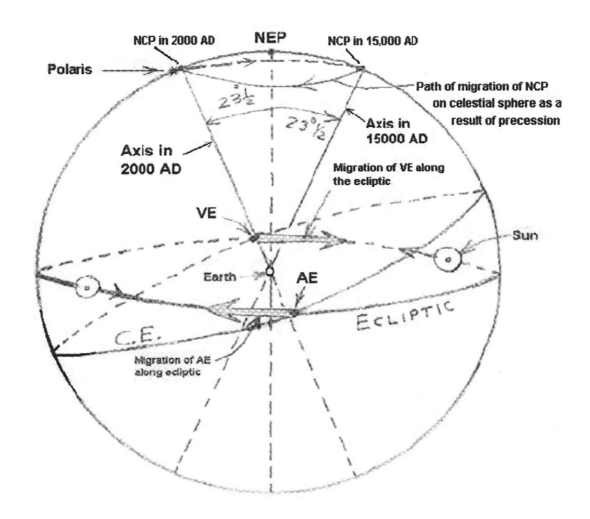

Since the Earth's axis is always perpendicular to the plane of the celestial equator, the celestial equator moves with respect to the fixed stars also. This in turn means the equinoxes slide along the ecliptic over the 26,000 year cycle as shown in the diagram.

Exercise 11.0

II. Tutorial

Log on to SKYLAB2 and select program No. 3, "PRECESSION". After you press the enter key, a polar projection star-chart centered on the North Ecliptic Pole (NEP) will appear on the screen, as shown on the next page. On the chart, circles concentric about the NEP are drawn every 10 degrees. Polaris (α UMi) is located about $24°$ from the NEP near the top of the chart. The position of the North Celestial Pole (NCP) is indicated by the yellow marker (a circle with a cross through it). This marker will be moving to animate the changing location of the NCP amongst the stars as a result of the precession of the Earth's axis. The location of the NCP corresponds to the date that continuously changes in the counter window to the upper left. Notice that the NCP is moving in a circular path around the NEP and, therefore, it is always a distance equal to $23.5°$ from the NEP. Remember, it is the precession of the Earth's axis that is causing this migration of the NCP.

Now type "D" to bring down the Date window and set the year to 1900. After you do this, bring down the Options window and change the step to 1 year and the delay factor to 0.2 seconds. When this is done and you press the Enter key, the position of the pole will be shown initially for 1900 and then the position will be shown for every year thereafter in 0.2 second intervals. Use the Space Bar to stop and start the motion to get a sense and feel for what is happening.

III. Assignment

Try to stop the migration of the NCP for the year when it is closest to Polaris. You may need to do this several times before you get the correct value. Remember, you can use the cursor left/right arrow keys to fast forward or reverse the motion. There will be a range of years over which you will not be able to tell any difference in the closest approach of the NCP to Polaris. Try to find out what this range is, and write these years here:

Range of Dates: _____.

The star chart shows the bright stars located along the path of the NCP around the NEP. After the NCP passes Polaris, in what year after that will the NCP be close to the relatively bright star β, which is in the constellation Cepheus, the king?

Year: _____.

When the ancient Egyptian engineers built the great pyramid of Cheops, they aligned one of the axes of the pyramid with the North Star. This could not have been Polaris. In fact it was the star called Thuban, which is in the constellation Draco. This star is labeled α **Dra** and is located $20°$ from the NEP in the 3 o'clock position on the chart. Assuming the pyramid was built when the NCP was closest to Thuban (it wasn't), what year was this? Be sure to run the position of the NCP closest to the star and not closest to the Greek letter.

Year: _____.

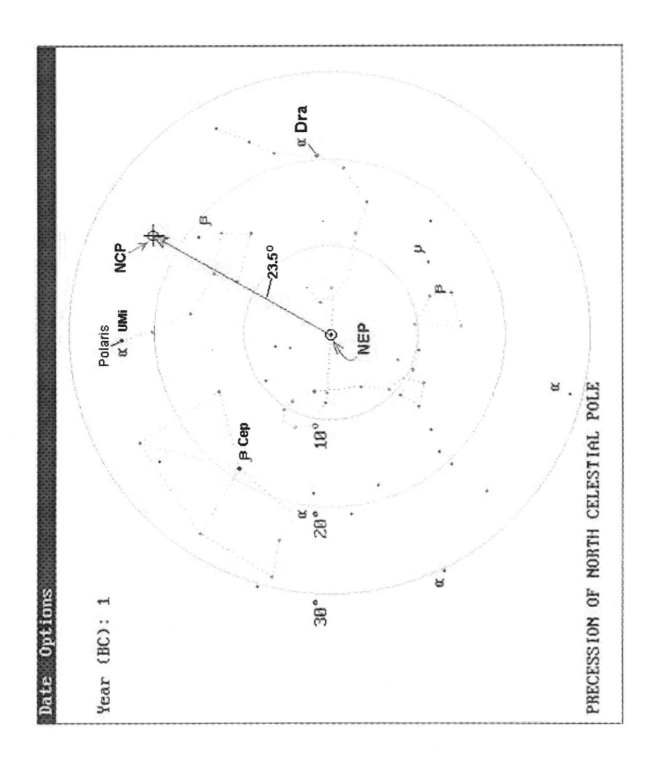

Exercise 12.0

TELESCOPIC OBSERVING

I. Properties And Use Of An Astronomical Telescope

The purpose of this experiment is to familiarize one with the use of an **equatorially mounted** telescope to locate celestial objects. The telescope is the tube and the optics contained within it. The telescope is mechanically attached to a set of perpendicular axels, each of which can be rotated independently. One of these axels is aligned with the axis of rotation of the Earth. Hence it points to the north celestial pole in the sky; for this reason it is called the **polar axel**. The other is called the **declination axel**. Motion of the instrument around the polar axis is done to change the right ascension or hour angle of the telescope. Motion of the telescope around the declination axis, changes the declination at which it is aimed. See the diagram on the next page.

Once the telescope is aimed at the object to be observed, it is necessary to compensate for the rotation of the Earth. This requires continuous motion of the telescope around the polar axis at the **sidereal rate**, which is accomplished by means of what is known as **a clock drive**. The clock drive is essentially an electric motor which, through a train of gears, provides a strong torque to turn the telescope around the polar axis at the sidereal rate. In addition, the telescope usually has manual or electrical **slow-motion controls** that enable the observer to make fine adjustments in the position of the telescope, in order to center a celestial object in the field of view.

Once an observer knows the approximate location of an object in one's horizon system, a small telescope such as the one you are using can be moved to point approximately in this direction. This is called **slewing** and if it is done by the observer, it is called **manual slewing**.

A small telescope is mounted on the tube of the larger telescope as a sight for quickly locating a target object. This auxiliary telescope is called the **finder telescope**. The finder telescope has a large field of view and low magnification. It is mounted in such a way that when the target is centered in the finder, the target should be nearly centered in the larger telescope.

On each axel of the main telescope is mounted a graduated circle or wheel called a **setting circle**. These are used for setting the telescope in right ascension and declination. As the telescope is turned around one of the axes, the coordinate at which the telescope is aimed can be read from a setting circle by an index or indicator. The declination circle is graduated in degrees and is always ready to be read. The right ascension circle, which is mounted on the polar axel near the clock drive housing, is larger and its smallest graduations may be a few minutes of time. The hours of right ascension (**RA**) are marked but usually that is all. However, each hour is divided in half and each half into quarters of an hour. On some telescopes divisions are every 10 minutes. You will have to determine the units for the smallest graduations by visual inspection.

Before the RA setting circle can be used, it must be turned and set to agree with the current sidereal time. There is usually a fiducial mark on the clock drive housing that indicates zero hour angle, and hence, the plane of the local celestial meridian (**LCM**). When the RA circle is turned so that this indicator lines up with the RA that is the same as the sidereal time, the circle is set to correctly read the RA at which the telescope is aimed. Once the circle is so set, it does not have be set again if the clock drive is running. This is because the clock drive also turns the RA circle at the sidereal rate. Hence, one needs a clock that keeps sidereal time in order to set a telescope. Such a clock is in the observatory, but it may not be correctly set. Hence, one needs to find the current sidereal time in some other way and check the clock. Once the clock is set for the day's observations, it will keep track of the sidereal time so that the observer can set his telescope to the RA of any object.

II. Procedure

Get a list of planetary positions for today's date. One source is the program "Ephemeris" available in the Skylab2 software. You can also get the local sidereal time from the program for the animation of the diurnal motion of the Sun under Skylab2's program "Celestial Sphere." In the latter program, change the date to the current one and the ZT to an exact hour value before the beginning of the observing session. When you go to set the sidereal clock in the observatory or the RA circle on the telescope to the correct LST, allow for the ZT that elapsed since you obtained the correct value of the LST.

Now turn the RA circle on your telescope until the current value of the LST is set to the LCM indicator. It is important to remember that:

The LST is the hour circle of RA currently aligned along the upper LCM.

The telescope is now ready to be slewed to the RA and DEC of the object you wish to observe. When you slew the telescope, make sure that the RA circle does not rotate and that it always reads the current LST.

Another way to set the RA circle is first to locate visually a bright star of known RA. Manually slew the telescope to acquire the star in the center of the field of view of the eyepiece, using the finder. Clamp the declination axel of the telescope and then turn the RA circle until the fiducial mark of the telescope is pointed to the RA of that star. The RA circle should now be set to the correct LST and an object of any RA may now be located.

Once you have acquired and centered the object you wish to observed in the field of view of the telescope, either manually or by means of the slow motion controls, tighten the RA and DEC clamps. The clock drive may not engage unless the RA clamp is sufficiently tight.

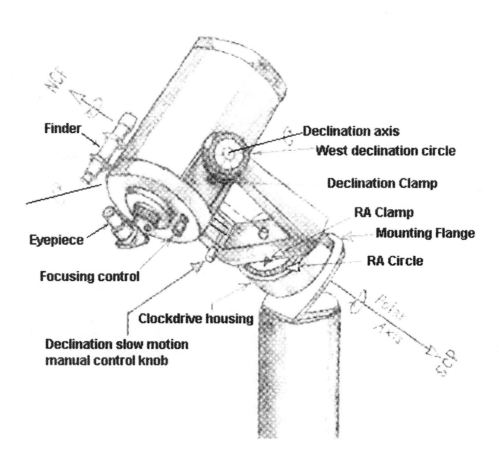

Exercise 13.0

LUNAR MOTION, ELONGATION, AND PHASES

I. Introduction

The Moon's revolution in orbit around the center of gravity (barycenter) of the Earth-Moon System results in an apparent motion of the Moon in the sky eastward relative to the Sun and, therefore, the **phases** of the Moon. When measured with respect to the fixed stars, the Moon's period of revolution is 27.3 days. That is, this is the length of time it takes the moon to revolve 360° in its orbit and is called the **Sidereal Month**. Hence, **the Moon's rate of motion is 13.20 degrees per day, eastward with respect to the fixed stars**. However, **the Moon's rate of motion is 12.20 degrees per day eastward with respect to the Sun**. This is because the Sun has an apparent motion eastward, along the ecliptic, of 1° per day with respect to the fixed stars. Recall that this apparent motion of the Sun is a reflection of the Earth's orbital motion around the Sun. The time it takes the moon to appear to move around the celestial sphere and return to the Sun is called the **Synodic Month**. This takes 29.5 days and is also the length of time it takes the moon to go through a complete cycle of its phases.

The Moon's orbital motion around the Earth causes the angle between the Sun and the Moon, as seen in the sky from the Earth, to continuously change. This angle is called **Elongation**.

Elongation is the angular distance of an object measured along the ecliptic, eastward or westward from the Sun.

When the Moon has a specific elongation, it has a specific phase, and rises and sets at a specific time. The table below lists the elongations of the Moon, the corresponding aspects or configuration names, and phases of the Moon.

Elongation	Aspect/Configuration	Phase
0°	Conjunction	New Moon
1 - 89° E		Waxing Crescent
90° E	Eastern Quadrature	First Quarter
91 - 179° E		Waxing Gibbous
180°	Opposition	Full Moon
179 - 91° W		Waning Gibbous
90° W	Western Quadrature	Third/Last Quarter
89 - 1° W		Waning Crescent

The approximate time the Moon rises for a given elongation can be calculated from the following equation:

Time of lunar event = Time for corresponding solar event - Elongation in time units.

This may be written in symbolic form as: $T_M = T_\odot - T_E$

For example, if we wanted to calculate what time the Moon will rise when it has a certain elongation, the corresponding time for the Sun would be sunrise. For sunrise use 6:00 and for sunset use 18:00. You should know what times to use for UT and LT of the Sun. For example, the full Moon, which has an elongation of $180°$ or 12^h, rises at sunset and sets at sunrise.

There can be more than an hour error in this calculation because the equation assumes that both the Sun and Moon are always on the celestial equator. Nevertheless, the above equation yields a good approximation, especially when the Sun and Moon are near the CE. The elongation angle, when expressed in time units, is simply the amount of time that the Moon lags the Sun, when the elongation is measured eastward, or precedes the Sun, when measured westward. In this exercise, we explore these relationships.

II. Tutorial

Logon to SKYLAB2 and select program SKYMATION. A rectangular chart will be drawn that represents the entire celestial sphere. The ecliptic appears as a wavy red curve. As soon as the chart is displayed, an animation will begin that shows the changing positions of the Sun, Moon, and planets in one day steps for the equatorial frame of reference. The positions of each of the planets, the Sun, and the Moon are indicated by small circles that are letter coded. The key to this code can be viewed as a window by typing "S" for symbols.

Open the Options window and select "Plot Stars." Now watch the animation run for a while to see what is happening and how the moon changes its position from day to day relative to the stars and the Sun. Note that the moon moves about 13 degrees eastward each day relative to the stars. Since the Sun moves eastward by 1 degree per day, the moon gains about 12 degrees per day on the Sun.

Recall that elongation is the angular distance of an object from the Sun as measured along the ecliptic. Watch the elongation of the moon changing. Occasionally press the space bar to stop the motion and see if you can estimate the Moon's elongation angle and direction. To do this, remember that each hour of RA is $15°$.

Now change the step size to 1 hour and delay factor to 0.5 second. This will enable you to see details happening over each day. Now allow the animation to begin. Note the planets hardly move at all in 1 hour, but the Moon's motion is noticeable.

The large jumps in the position of the LCM are the result of seeing where it is relative to the stars every hour and thereby indicating the sidereal time for the corresponding ZT indicated at the top of the screen. This eastward motion of the LCM is an alternative way of representing diurnal motion of the celestial sphere westward relative to the LCM. Recall that the parallels of declination are the diurnal circles.

Now we shall animate the Moon's daily motion in another way. From the main menu of SKYLAB2, select Lunamation. Then from the Lunamation Menu, select NO. 2, Diurnal Motion. Now a diagram will appear on the screen with three different panels. The center panel represents an observer-centered diagram of the horizon system, as seen projected into the plane of the prime vertical. The diurnal circles of the Sun and Moon are shown to be one and the same. The horizontal line with east on the left and west on the right is meant to represent the east-west line in the plane of the celestial horizon. The vertical line represents the plane of the LCM with upper transit at the top and lower transit at the bottom. The observer is located at the center of the diurnal circle.

The animation depicts the diurnal motion of the Sun and Moon around the observer from east to west. This is the result of the rotation of the celestial sphere (or Earth). At the same time, the orbital motion of the moon around the Earth shows up as a slow eastward displacement of the moon relative to the Sun at the rate of 12.2 degrees per day (13.2 degrees per day with respect to the fixed stars). The angle between the Sun and the LCM indicates the local apparent solar time, LAT. The angle between the Sun and the moon, as

Exercise 13.0

measured along the circle of motion, is the Moon's elongation. This angle is related to the phase of the moon.

The lower left panel shows a view of the phase of the Moon as we would see it in the sky. The panel on the lower right is a view of the Moon's position in its orbit relative to the Earth; the direction of the Sun is to the right. This view is from a point in space far above the plane of the Moon's orbit.

At the top right of the screen are given the date and the ZT. Watch the animation continue through one lunar cycle or more, until you understand these motions. The animation can be stopped and started by pressing the space bar. Try to run the animation at a speed where you can stop the animation just as the moon rises or sets. Note that the time the moon rises or sets depends on the elongation or phase of the moon. Both of these events are retarded by about 48.8 minutes from the previous day (12.2 deg. x 4 min/deg.). When you have gained experience running the lunamation program, you are ready to advance to Part III.

III. Assignment

A. Determining the Lunar Orbital period

Run the program Skymation with the step size set to 3 hours and a delay time of 0.6 seconds. Plot the stars and a grid. Now set Skylab to trail the Moon's motion (under Options) and then quickly press the space bar to halt the animation. Now get a printout (#1)

On the answer sheet, write down the day and time (ZT) as answer No. 1. Also take careful note of the position of the Moon with respect to the stars and record the Moon's RA in hours and minutes and DEC. in degrees and record these values on the answer sheet.

Now start the animation and allow the Moon to complete exactly one orbit relative to the fixed stars and then press the space bar to stop the motion when the Moon returns to the position recorded above. Do not allow the moon to move past this point. You may have to practice before you are able to do this! Record the date and time when this happens on the answer sheet as No. 2 and get a hardcopy of the screen. The two dates that you have recorded will be analyzed later.

B. Determining Moonrise and Moonset

Now we shall investigate the diurnal and orbital motions of the Moon and the resulting changes in the Moon's elongation and rising and setting. To do this, run the Diurnal Motion program under Lunamation. Set the step size to 4 min. and the delay factor to 0.80 seconds. In this way you should be able to determine the time of moonrise or moonset with a precision of 4 minutes. Now run the program and stop the animation when the center of the moon is just rising or setting (at the East or West Point) for the date assigned to you. Get a printout of this screen (#3).

Now we shall watch the diurnal motion of the moon and planets in the horizon system. Exit Lunamation and activate the Skymation program. When the animation begins change the date to the one that is a few days earlier than the one you have been using above. Set the step size to 4 min. and the delay factor to 0.80 sec. After you return to the animation again, type "C" to open the coordinates menu, then select "Horizon" and press Enter. Now pan up by 15°, and then zoom out by a factor of 3. This will provide a more panoramic view of the horizon system.

Allow the animation to run and watch the planets move along their diurnal circles relative to the horizon and LCM. The latter is the red vertical line fixed at azimuth 180. Recall that the east point of the horizon is at azimuth 90 and west is at 270.   Notice that the planets rise from the east, ascend to upper transit on the LCM, and then descend to set in the west.   This motion represents their diurnal circles in the horizon system. Watch the animation for a few days or until you understand what is taking place.

Remain in the horizon system and under the Options menu, select to trail the Moon. **Do not request a grid or plot the stars, otherwise the Moon will not trail.** Allow the animation to continue and watch the changing diurnal circle of the moon from one day to the next.   This results from the fact that the orbit of the Moon is inclined to the plane of the celestial equator and its declination is changing.   Now reset the date to the one assigned and try to stop the animation when the Moon either rises or sets (altitude=0°). Obtain a hardcopy of the screen (#4) and write the ZT on the answer sheet as No. 11.   Does this value agree with the ZT value at the top of printout #3? If not, you should be able to explain why not. Hint: consider the declination of the Moon and Sun and the difference between ZT and LAT.   Answer No. 11 is the more correct answer.

Proceed to analyze the charts you have obtained:

No. 3. Convert the minutes and hours that you recorded for answers Nos. 1 and 2 to a decimal part of a day.   Then record the difference in days and decimal parts thereof as the answer to No. 3 on the answer sheet. Show your calculation at the bottom of the answer page.

No. 4   The above answer is the time it takes the Moon to complete one orbit. What is this period of the Moon's motion called? To answer, think about how the position of the Moon was determined and compare with the definitions of the two kinds of lunar orbital periods given in the introduction.

No. 5. Now take hardcopy #3 and draw a line from the observer to the center of the Sun and another line from the observer to the center of the Moon. The angle between these two lines is the elongation of the Moon. Measure this angle with your protractor and record along with the direction.

Draw an arc from the Sun to the Moon in a way similar to that shown in the sample chart at the end of this exercise. Draw an arrowhead at the Moon and print the elongation of the moon along this arc as shown in the sample diagram. Be sure to indicate whether the elongation is E/W. The value of the elongation of the moon that you have measured should agree with the phase of the Moon given in the lower left panel of the page. If they do not agree, you are doing something incorrectly.

No. 6. Now take the value you measured for the elongation of the Moon and covert the degrees to hours and minutes of time using the angular rate of rotation of the Earth. ⋅ Prefix the proper algebraic sign depending on whether the elongation is east or west of the Sun.

No. 7. Use the above value and the equation in section **I** to calculate the LAT at which the Moon rose or set. Show the steps of your calculation in the upper left hand corner of chart #3 exactly as shown on the sample chart. Also record your answer on the answer page.

No. 8. On chart #3, draw an arc from the point of upper transit to the Sun to represent the hour angle of the Sun. Place an arrowhead at the Sun to indicate the sense of direction. Use you protractor to measure this angle and record this as No. 8 on the answer page with the correct direction. Also label and write the value of the hour angle along the arc exactly as shown in the sample.

Exercise 13.0

> **No. 9**. Convert the above hour angle of the Sun to hours and minutes of time using the angular rate of rotation of the Earth, as you did for the Moon's elongation. Record this on the answer page.

> **No. 10**. Now use this value and the equation:

$$LAT = HA_O + 12:00$$

> to compute the LAT for the Moon to rise or set another way. Show this calculation in the top, right corner of chart #3, following each step exactly as shown on the sample chart. Also record your answer on the answer page.

The answers to No. 7 and No. 10 should agree within 4 minutes. Compare these results with the value of the ZT displayed at the top right of the chart. The difference between the ZT and your two values may differ by up to 90 minutes or so. Part of this difference is the equation of time (Exercise 8.0). There are also contributions from the obliquity of the ecliptic, the inclination of the Moon's orbit, and the distortion of the Moon's diurnal circle on chart #3 introduced by the software and printer.

Also compare the answer in No. 11 with your two calculated values. They may not agree with this either because of the assumptions necessary for the above equations to be valid. No. 11 is probably the most accurate value.

Exercise 13.0

Lunar Motion Answer Sheet

1. Date to begin Moon's motion: Date _____ ; ZT_____ .

   Moon's position on printout 1:   RA _____ ; DEC _____ .

2. Date of end of Moon's motion (Must be at the same RA and DEC as above):

   Date_____ ; ZT_____ .

3. Time for one lunar orbit in days and decimal parts thereof (Show calculation below):

   _____ .

4. Name of Period (See Sec. I):   _____ .

5. Lunar Elongation in degrees as measured on printout #3:   _____ .

6. Above elongation of the Moon converted to hours and minutes, T_E: _____ .

7. Calculated LAT of Moon rise/set using $T_M = T_\odot - T_E$:   _____ .

8. Hour angle of the Sun in degrees as measured on printout #3:   _____ .

9. Hour angle of the Sun converted to hours and minutes: _____ .

10. Computed LAT from above hour angle of Sun, using LAT = $HA_\odot$ + 12:00 :   _____ .

11. Moonrise/set from horizon system printout (#4):   _____ .

Show here the details of the calculation for the answer to #3:

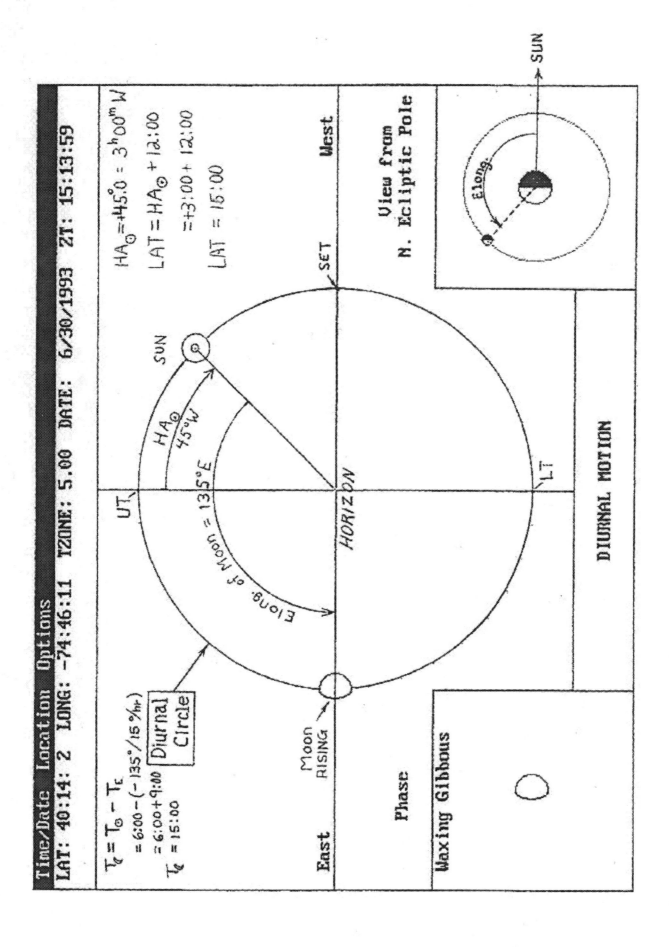

Exercise 13.2

APPARENT PLANETARY POSITIONS

1. Logon to **Skylab2** and run the program "SKYMATION." Select a date and time that you want to observe the planets. Do not pick a date near new moon. Call for a "grid" and "plot stars" under Options. Get a printout of this chart.

2. Use a flexible ruler or cardboard strip and bend it to conform to the ecliptic between the vernal and autumnal equinoxes on the chart and measure this distance in cm. Make sure your measurement has hundredth place precision. Record your measurement on the answer page. Recall that the distance you have just measured is equivalent to an angle of $180°$ along the ecliptic.

3. Now divide $180°$ by the distance you have measured in step 2. This will be the chart scale in degrees per centimeter for measuring elongations along the ecliptic. Record the result on the answer page with a precision of at least four significant figures.

4. Draw a short line from the Moon to the closest point on the ecliptic and mark this point. Use your flexible ruler and bend it to conform to the shape of the ecliptic to measure the distance from the center of the Sun to the above point. Write the answer on the answer sheet. This is the elongation of the Moon in centimeters either east or west.

5. Multiply the above distance by the chart scale you have determined. This will be the elongation of the Moon in degrees east or west. Write the answer on the answer page.

6. What is the phase of the Moon corresponding to this elongation? Record your answer.

7. Follow the above procedure and determine the elongation of Venus. Record your answer:

8. How many degrees will the Moon move in its orbit with respect to the fixed stars in 8 days and in what direction? Record your answer.

9. Locate the point on the chart where the Moon will be in 8 days and label this point as **L8**.

10. Locate the new position of the Sun for 8 days later and label this point as **H8**.

11. Now determine the elongation of the Moon for 8 days later following the above procedure and record your answer on the answer page.

12. What is the phase of the Moon now, eight days later? Record your answer.

EXERCISE 13.2 ANSWER PAGE

APPARENT PLANETARY MOTIONS

1. Date and ZT time of your chart:: Date_____ Time_____.

2. Distance along ecliptic between equinoxes: _____.

3. Elongation chart scale: _____.

4. Elongation of Moon in centimeters east or west: _____ .

5. Elongation of Moon is degrees east or west: _____.

6. Phase of the Moon: _____.

7. Elongation of Venus: _____ .

8. Distance in degrees that the Moon will move in its orbit: _____.

11. Elongation of the Moon eight days later: _____ .

12. Phase of the Moon eight days later: _____ .

Exercise 14.0

ECLIPSES

I. Introduction

There are two kinds of eclipses, **solar** and **lunar.** Each of these can be either a **total** eclipse or a **partial** eclipse, depending on the exact geometric alignment of the Sun and Moon in the sky as seen from the observer's location on the Earth. Furthermore, lunar eclipses are also described as being either **umbral** or **penumbral**, depending on what part of the Earth's shadow is involved. A solar eclipse happens at lunar conjunction, when the Moon passes in front of the Sun. A lunar eclipse occurs at lunar opposition, when the Moon passes through the Earth's shadow.

Because the orbital plane of the Moon is inclined 5° with respect to the plane of the ecliptic, an eclipse does not occur every new moon or full moon. The latter events must happen when the Sun is sufficiently near one of the points of intersection of the Moon's orbit with the ecliptic. These points are called the lunar orbital nodes, or **LON**, and are 180° apart. When the Sun is within a certain angular distance of a node, such that an eclipse is possible, it is said to be an eclipse season. The angular **windows**, centered on each node, within which the Sun and Moon must be for an eclipse to occur are called the eclipse limits. The eclipse limits are 12° E/W of a node for a lunar eclipse (see diagram below) and 18° E/W from a node for a solar eclipse. Since the Sun has an average daily motion of 1° along the ecliptic, a lunar eclipse season lasts 24 days since the eclipse window is 24 degrees wide. A solar eclipse season is 36 days long, since the window is 36 degrees wide.

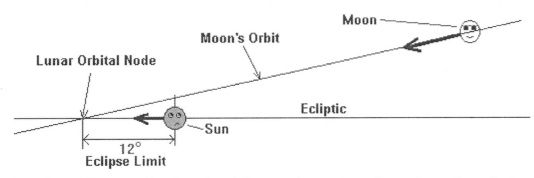

In the above diagram, the Sun is at the western edge of a solar eclipse limit. The angular distance of the Moon from the Sun (the Moon's elongation) is about 45° W. Since the Moon moves eastward in its orbit at a rate of 13.2° per day and the Sun moves eastward along the ecliptic only 1° per day, the Moon will catch up to the Sun in 3.7 days (45°/12.2 deg./day). By this time the Sun has moved only 3.7° to the east and will be within the eclipse limit. So at conjunction, a solar eclipse will occur. This demonstrates in a very simple way how eclipses may be predicted in advance.

The Sun disturbs the motion of the Moon in such a way that its orbit gyrates around the Earth once every 18.61 years. That is, the line passing through the Earth and connecting the nodes rotates clockwise in the plane of ecliptic. Hence, the nodes slowly slide westward along the ecliptic. This motion is called the **regression of the lunar orbital nodes**. The motion of nodes must be taken into account when predicting eclipse. The regression of the lunar orbital nodes causes the eclipse seasons to arrive 2.7 weeks earlier each successive year.

II. Tutorial

After you logon to Skylab2, select the program "Lunamation". From the Lunamation menu, select "Eclipse". After you press the Enter key, a screen will appear showing 4 panels. These list the location of the observer, the time, date, and elevation for which the computer will calculate and demonstrate eclipses. The default values are for TCNJ. The bottom panel shows a box containing "SAVE/CONT" to be highlighted. Unless you want to change the default parameters, press Enter. A table will then flash on the screen briefly and you may be able to see the computer adding lines of data to it, as all lunar conjunctions and oppositions are calculated for the 8 month period following the current date. You can ignore this, since another table will immediately replace this one, with the results of these calculations when they are completed. In the final table, the first column lists the date of the lunar event, the second column gives the zone time, the third and fourth columns can be ignored, the fifth column gives the phase of the Moon, and the sixth column provides information on whether there is an eclipse and its visibility. If the Comments column says that an eclipse is visible at this location, an animation of the eclipse is available.

The parenthetical notes "(CV)" and "(OV)" mean that the opposition or conjunction is visible and an animation is available, though there is no eclipse. To see any of these, use the cursor key to highlight the date of the event and press the Enter key. Select such an event and do this now. This will bring up a screen that shows a rectangular chart of the region of the celestial sphere where the event will take place. An example of what the chart should look like is at the end of this exercise.

On your monitor screen, the red dashed curve is the ecliptic. Centered on the ecliptic is either the Sun or a cross-section of the Earth's shadow at the distance of the Moon from the Earth, depending on whether you are viewing a solar or lunar eclipse. The green dotted curve is the Moon's orbit.

An animation of the Moon's motion along its orbit, relative to the stars, begins immediately. The motion of the Sun or Earth's shadow is frozen to simplify matters. The zone time will be displayed to the right in the bar-panel at the top of the chart. The zone time when the conjunction or opposition occurs is given in blue at the bottom left corner of the screen.

Now use the space bar to stop the motion at the exact time of the conjunction or opposition. The screen will now show the locations of the Moon and Sun (or Earth's shadow) relative to one another at the exact instant of either of these two events.

Make careful note of the following: The Moon lies along a line passing through the Sun (or cross-section of the Earth's shadow) and that this line is perpendicular to the ecliptic, and not necessarily parallel to the hour circles of RA. This alignment corresponds to a lunar elongation of $0°$ for a conjunction or $180°$ for an opposition, whether or not there is an eclipse.

Now allow the animation to run and watch what happens. Ask yourself if you completely understand what you see happening. If not, you probably need to refer to your class notes and the textbook on eclipses. Work back and forth until you do understand. Lack of understanding often occurs as a result of not knowing the terminology.

III. Assignment

You will now investigate the nodes of the Moon's orbit. Starting from today's date, run the program Skymation with a step size equal to 6 hours and a delay time of 0.6 seconds. Plot the stars and grid. Now trail the Moon's motion. Allow the Moon to continue its motion until it closes its orbit, then stop the motion. Get a printout of this screen (#1). Now note the two points where the Moon's orbit crosses the ecliptic on this printout or on the screen. These are the lunar orbital nodes (LON). The point where the Moon crosses the ecliptic from above or north of the ecliptic to south of the ecliptic is called the **descending node**. The other is the **ascending node**.

No. 1. Turn off trailing the Moon and then allow the animation to continue. Watch the Sun's motion. Search through the year, running the Sun backwards or forwards as necessary until the Sun, in turn, it is at each of the lunar orbital nodes. (Use printout #1 to assist you, noting the RA and Dec. for each node). Stop the motion and record these dates on the answer page.

No. 2. What is the significance of the above two dates for the eclipse seasons?

Exercise 14.0 Continued

No. 3. Now select the subprogram Eclipse under Lunamation. Go to the screen with the "Location and Date" panels. Press the cursor-up key to get to the "Zone Time/Date" line and change the date to 11-01-1993. Press the Enter key until the window with SAVE/CONT is highlighted and then press Enter one more time. When the "Solar and Lunar Eclipse" Table appears, look at the entries. There is an eclipse on 11-13-1993 but it is not visible from TCNJ. What is the phase of the Moon on 11-13-1993? Write your response on the answer page.

No. 4. Make sure the above date is highlighted and press Enter. A screen now appears giving the lunar aspect or configuration name. What is the lunar event or aspect? The answer is there on the screen but you have to associate the term aspect with one of the words.

Now press Enter to get back to the Table. Use the cursor key to highlight the date 12-28-1993. Note the lunar phase. Press Enter and watch the animation. Stop the Moon when the ZT is the same as that shown at the lower left for this event. Obtain a print-out of the screen (#2). Take careful note again of the alignment of the Moon with the Earth's shadow and the ecliptic. Do you see why there is no eclipse? Answer the following using this screen:

No. 5. Where is the nearest lunar orbital node, to the right or to the left of the screen?

No. 6. Is this the ascending or descending node?

The curvature of the ecliptic and the Moon's orbit make it difficult to measure how far the Sun or Earth's shadow is from the node but you should be able to judge that it is outside the eclipse limit. Remember that the latter is 12° E/W of a lunar orbital node for a lunar eclipse and 18° E/W for a solar eclipse.

Now view the eclipse of 11-29-1993 to see an example of a total lunar eclipse. Note that the Earth's shadow consists of two regions, the umbra and penumbra. When any part of the Moon enters the umbra, no sunlight reaches that part of the Moon. In the penumbra, the Moon receives partial illumination.

Now view the eclipse of 5-10-1994 to see an example of a nearly total solar eclipse. The latter is a good example of an **annular eclipse**. This is when the Moon appears too small to cover the Sun because the Moon is near **apogee** in its orbit. View the animation of the partial lunar umbral eclipse of 5-24-1994. Make sure you are able to explain why this is not a total eclipse. Look at the trajectory of the Moon through the Earth's shadow and note the distance of the nearest lunar orbital node. Answer the following:

No. 7. Is this eclipse occurring at an ascending or descending node?

No. 8. Is this eclipse one of maximum duration? Explain. Look at the trajectory or path the Moon takes through the Earth's shadow and relate this to the distance of the lunar orbital node. In your answer compare these two things to what the scenario should be for a better eclipse.

No. 9. Run the animation for the eclipse of 03-23-97. Obtain a printout (#3) at the middle of the eclipse. What type of eclipse is this? Be sure you identify the eclipse thoroughly using all the necessary adjectives. See the 1st paragraph of Section I.

Now press **Esc** twice to go back to the screen for changing the date. Change the date to 01-01-2007 and press **Enter** until the table of eclipses appears. Answer the following:

No. 10. List on the answer sheet the dates of all eclipses in the first half of the year. These should be the eclipses that are occurring in the first eclipse season of the year. If the table says "No eclipse visible at this location" there is an eclipse but if the table says "No eclipse visible at any location" then no eclipse occurs.

Return to the screen for changing the location and date, and change the date to 07-01-2007 in order to get the tabular listing of the eclipses for the 2nd half of this year. Record these on the answer sheet in the column for the eclipses of the second eclipse season in the year. Remember, the eclipse seasons are about 6 months apart. Note that all the eclipses listed for a given season are within 36 days of one another. Beware of there being part of a 3rd eclipse season in a year. Do not list such eclipses.

Now find all the eclipses for 2011, as you did for 2007, and list them on the answer sheet. Again, separate the eclipses for 2011 into 2 columns, one for each eclipse season.

No. 11. Search to find the date for the next total lunar eclipse that is visible after today at this location. Write the answer on the answer page.

No. 12. Search for the date of the next solar eclipse, of any type, that is visible at this location after today's date. Hint: It occurs more than 5 years from 2010. Record on the answer page.

Now proceed to analyze the charts that you have printed.

No. 13. Write down the approximate RA and DEC coordinates of the two lunar orbital nodes from printout #1, distinguishing the ascending node from the descending one.

No. 14. Use a flexible ruler or cardboard strip and bend it to conform to the ecliptic between the vernal and autumnal equinoxes on printout #1 to measure this distance in cm. Make sure your measurement has hundredth place precision. Record your measurement on the answer page. This distance is equivalent to an angle of 180°.

No.15. Use the above data to calculate the chart scale for measuring elongations along the ecliptic. Record the result on the answer page.

No. 16. Bend your flexible ruler to measure the separation of the nodes along the ecliptic in cm and record on the answer page. Then use the above chart scale to convert this distance to degrees. Record your results on the answer page.

No. 17. Refer to the chart at the end of this exercise for the eclipse of 5-24-1994. How far away in degrees is the nearest lunar node? You will need to extrapolate off the page, using another piece of paper. Use the RA scale to assist your measurement. Recall that every tenth of an hour is 1.5°.

No. 18. Now examine the two sets of eclipse dates for 2007 from No. 10. These represent each of the two eclipse seasons for 2007. If there is only one eclipse listed for a given eclipse season, assume it occurs at the middle of the season. If there are 2 eclipses, assume the middle of the season is midway between the two eclipses. If there are 3, assume the middle of the season is the same date as the 2nd eclipse. Determine the middle date of each eclipse season in 2007 and record on the answer page.

No. 19. Compare the middle dates for the two eclipse seasons. How far apart in months are these seasons?

Exercise 14.0 Continued

> **No. 20**. Recalling that each eclipse season is about 36 days long, estimate the beginning and end dates for each season, using the middle date.

> **No. 21**. Determine the middle date for each of the two eclipse seasons in the year 2011.

> **No. 22**. Estimate the beginning and end dates for each eclipse season in 2011 as you did for 2007.

> **No. 23**. Compare the middle dates for the eclipse seasons in 2007 with those in 2011. Recall that a given eclipse season comes earlier each year. Compute by how much the above eclipse seasons have shifted in weeks over the 4 years and how much per year.

> **No. 24**. What is the technical name for this shift?

> **No. 25**. What causes this phenomenon to happen?

> **No. 26**. Use printout #2 and determine the time of opposition of the Moon. Record you result on the answer page.

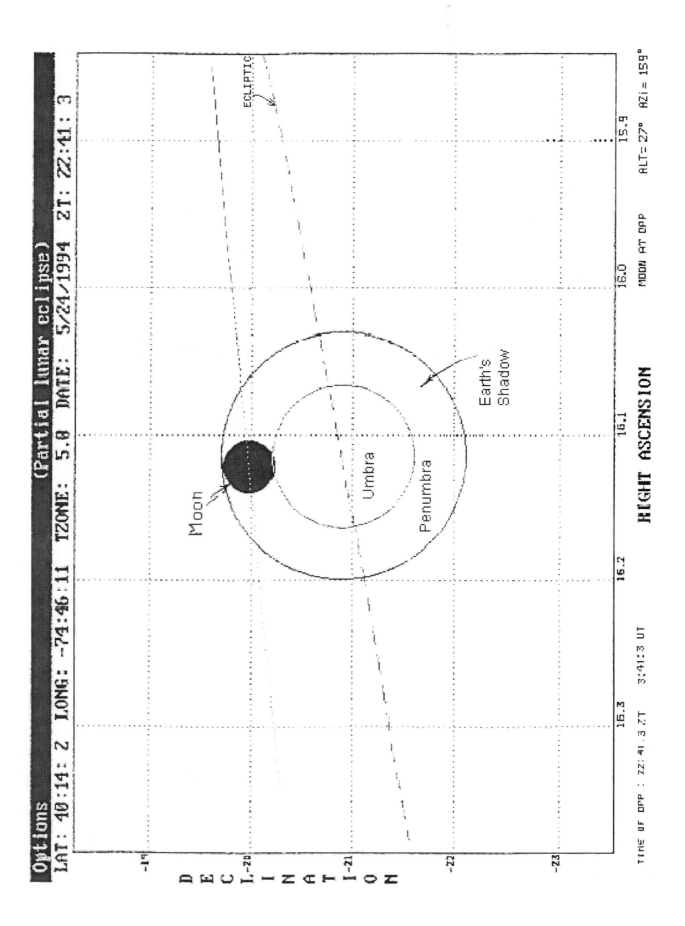

Options

LAT: 40:14: 2 LONG: -74:46:11 TZONE: 5.0 DATE: 5/24/1994 ZT: 22:41: 3 (Partial lunar eclipse)

ECLIPTIC

Earth's
Shadow

Umbra

Penumbra

Moon

DECLINATION

-19°
-20°
-21
-22
-23

RIGHT ASCENSION

15.9   16.0   16.1   16.2   16.3

TIME OF OPP : 22:41:3 ZT   3:41:3 UT   MOON AT OPP   ALT= 27°   AZi= 159°

ANSWER PAGES FOR EXERCISE 14.0 ON ECLIPSES

1. Date sun at ascending node: _____ ; at descending node: _____ .

2. Significance of above dates is_____
   _____

3. Phase of the Moon: _____ .

4. Lunar event or aspect: _____ .

5. Location of nearest lunar orbital node: _____ .

6. Identification of node: _____

7. Identification of node: _____ .

8. Considering the angular distance of the Earth's shadow from the nearest node and the line the Moon follows through the shadow, why is or isn't this an umbral eclipse that is of maximum duration?

9. Type of eclipse: _____ .

10.   Eclipses in 2007   Eclipses in 2011
        1st season   2nd season   1st season   2nd season

11. Next lunar eclipse visible from here: _____ .

12. Next solar eclipse visible at this location: _____ .

13. Coordinates of lunar nodes: Ascending node: RA_____ Dec_____ .

    Descending node: RA _____ Dec_____ .

14. Measured distance along ecliptic in cm between the VE & AE: _____ .

15. Elongation chart scale: _____ (deg./cm).

Exercise 14.0. Answer Page 2

16. Separation of nodes along ecliptic in cm: _____ ; in degrees:_____ .

17. Angular distance of nearest lunar orbital node from the center of the cross-section of the Earth's shadow for the eclipse of 5-24-1994 :

_____ .

18. The middle dates for each season in 2007 are _____ and _____ .

19. Time interval between middle dates for each eclipse seasons in 2007: _____ .

20. The beginning and end dates for each of the eclipse seasons for the year 2007 are:

_____ to _____ , and _____ to _____ .

21. Middle dates for each eclipse season in 2011 are_____ and _____ .

22. Time interval between middle dates for each eclipse seasons in 2011: _____ .

23. The beginning and end dates for each of the eclipse seasons for the year 2011 are:

_____ to _____ , and _____ to _____ .

24. Amount the eclipse seasons shifted in weeks between the above years is: _____ .

The amount of shift per year is: _____

25. Astronomical name for this shift: _____ .

26. Cause of the shift in the eclipse seasons: _____

_____

_____ .

27. Zone time of lunar opposition from printout #2: _____ .

Exercise 14.5

REGRESSION OF THE LUNAR ORBITAL NODES

I. The Moon's Orbit.

Log on to **SKYLAB2** and select the program *SKYMATION*. When the star chart appears and the animation of the planetary motions begins, call down the Options menu, select "Grid", and press "Enter."

Open the Options window again, select "Step", and press enter. Set the step size to 15 minutes and press enter. Now set the "Delay" time to 0.5.

Open the Options window a third time and now select "Trail" and press Enter. This will open another menu that lists the planets. Cursor to highlight the Moon and then press Enter until the animation begins. The Moon's motion will now be trailed thereby revealing its orbit on the chart.

Allow the animation to continue for one month or until the Moon comes back to where the orbit closes on itself. Quickly press the space bar to stop the motion.

Now inspect the Moon's orbit and its relation to the ecliptic. Recall that the Moon's orbit is inclined 5o to the ecliptic and that what you see on the screen is how this inclination is represented on a flat chart of the sky. You should be able to see that the Moon's motion in its orbit is such that the Moon is always close to the ecliptic in the sky. Notice that there are two places where the Moon's orbit crosses the ecliptic. These points are called the **nodes of the Moon's orbit**. The **ascending node** is the point where the Moon crosses the ecliptic moving from south to north of the ecliptic. The **descending node** is the point where the Moon crosses the ecliptic moving from north to south of the ecliptic.

Read off the RA (hours and minutes) and DEC (degrees) of these two points and record them here:

Ascending Node: RA_____; DEC._____.

Descending Node: RA_____; DEC._____.

Because the Sun and equatorial bulge of the Earth gravitationally perturb the moon's orbit, the lunar orbital nodes **regress** (move westward) along the ecliptic, making a complete circuit in about 19 years. Now you will investigate this regression and make a more accurate determination of the time for the nodes to move 360 degrees around the celestial sphere.

II. Investigating Regression

Assuming you have not changed the screen since you stopped the Moon's motion above. Press "P" twice, to Pan. Highlight "Right", and press Enter. Change the number of units to 6 and press Enter. Now press "Z" and then highlight "Zoom In". Make sure the zoom factor is 2x, and press Enter.

Now press "T", change the date to Oct. 15, 2004, and press Enter.

Wait for the Moon to enter the screen from the right. As soon as the Moon crosses the ecliptic, stop the motion and record this as the initial date:

Initial Date _____.   Final Date:_____ .

Since the Moon is making one day (13.20 degree) jumps every fraction of a second, you will probably stop the motion one day late. Reduce the step size and/or increase the delay time to one convenient for determining the exact day.

Allow the moon to trail to the left side of the screen and immediately press "T". Reset the date to Oct. 1, 2008; press Enter,

Wait for the Moon to enter from the right. As soon as it crosses the ecliptic again press the space bar to stop the motion and record the date above as the final one.

Now allow the motion to continue until the moon trails off to the left of the screen, then stop the motion. You should now see the two positions of the same node separated by almost four years. Notice which way the node has moved over this time interval. Stop to mentally affirm that this agrees with what you have previously learned about the regression. **Get a printout of this screen.**

Now we want to know how much the node has moved in degrees. In order to do this, it will be necessary to determine the chart scale for measuring angular distances along the ecliptic. Use a flexible ruler and bend it to follow the curvature of the ecliptic in order to measure the distance (to the hundredth of a cm) between the solstice and the equinox. You should be able to locate these points; if you have forgotten, refer back to exercise on the diurnal circles of the Sun.

You should also know the angular separation of these two points on the ecliptic. Now calculate the chart scale in deg/cm.

Chart Scale along ecliptic: _____deg/cm.

Now measure the distance between the position of the node in 2004 and in 2008 with the flexible ruler. Use the above chart scale to convert to degrees. Record your results below:

Distance between nodes in cm: _____.

Distance between nodes in degrees _____.

Now determine exactly how many days there are between the two dates you recorded above for the moon crossing the ecliptic

Time interval in days: _____.

Divide the above result by 365.25 days to convert this time to years. Record the result below with two decimal places of precision:

Time interval in years: _____ .

Compute the rate of the regression by dividing the number of years by the number of degrees that the node has moved. This yields the number of years it takes to move one degree. (You should know whether this number is less than or greater than one year before you do the calculation, since you already know the approximate value for the regression cycle. Think this through!) Record this number below.

Rate of regression: _____.

Now multiply the above rate of regression 360° to get the regression period. Record the value below:

Period of regression of the lunar orbital nodes: _____.

Compare your answer agree with the value given in the book.

Exercise 15.0

PLANETARY ORBITS AND CONFIGURATIONS

I. Introduction

The planets revolve around the Sun in orbits that lie nearly in the same plane. Therefore, the planets, with the exception of Pluto, are always found in the belt of the sky called the Zodiac, which is centered on the ecliptic and extends about 8° on each side of it. (Pluto can be as much as 17° away from the ecliptic.) Planets closer to the Sun than the Earth are classified as **Inferior planets.** Those planets farther from the Sun than the Earth are classified as **Superior Planets.** The apparent motion of a planet against the background stars depends on whether the planet is an inferior or a superior planet.

The angular separation of the Sun and a planet as seen from the Earth and measured east or west along the ecliptic is called the planet's elongation.

Elongation is the angular distance of an object from the Sun.

It is important to remember that **eastern elongations are negative numbers** and **western elongations are positive numbers.**

Certain specific elongation values are given names called *Aspects* or *Configurations*.

When two objects are in the same direction as seen from the Earth (Elongation = 0°), the aspect is **Conjunction.** When an object and the Sun are observed to be 90° apart (Elongation = 90° east or west) the object's aspect is **Eastern Quadrature** or **Western Quadrature.** When two objects are observed to be in opposite directions (Elongation = 180°) the aspect is **Opposition.**

The diagram on the right depicts the plane of the Earth's orbit as viewed from the north ecliptic pole. Drawn in this plane are examples of the orbits of a superior planet and an inferior planet relative to the Earth's orbit. In such a diagram, elongation is the angle between a line drawn from the Earth to the Sun and another line drawn from the Earth to the planet that is to be observed. **The vertex of the elongation angle is always at the center of the Earth, not at the Sun.** In the same diagram, westward is in the clockwise direction and eastward is counterclockwise.

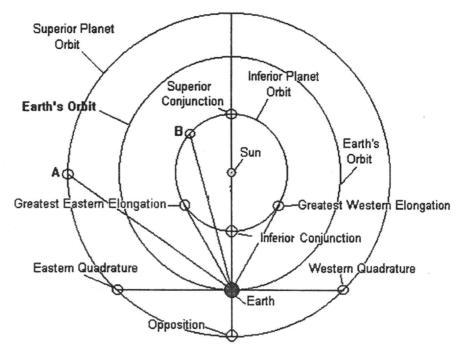

For inferior planets there is a maximum angular distance the planet can be observed from the

Sun. This angle can be found by drawing a line from the center of the Earth to a point on the planet's orbit such that this line is perpendicular to a radius of the orbit. Such a line is called a tangent line. These maximum angles for an inferior planet are called **greatest eastern elongation** or **greatest western elongation**. They must always be less than 90^0. Since an inferior planet's orbit lies within the Earth's orbit, it can never be at opposition (Elongation = 180^0) or quadrature (Elongation = 90^0). However, an inferior planet has two types of conjunction. One is when the planet is closest to the Earth, i.e., between the Earth and the Sun. This is called an **inferior conjunction**. The other is when the planet is on the far side of the Sun. This is called a **superior conjunction**.

The motion of a superior planet carries it through a complete range of elongations, similar to the Moon. When a superior planet is at opposition, it is closest to the Earth, and when it is at conjunction (by the geometry a superior conjunction) it is farthest from the Earth.

There is a simple relation between a planet's elongation and the approximate time it will rise, make upper transit (UT), or set. This is:

$$T_P = T_\odot - T_E$$

The meaning of the symbols in the above equation is as follows:

T_P = Local Time when a planet will rise, make upper transit, etc.
$T_\odot$ = Local Time for the corresponding solar event: rise, set, etc.
T_E = Planetary elongation in time units.

This equation works best when the planet and the Sun are both near the celestial equator. We can then assume that sunrise is 06:00, upper transit (UT) for the Sun is 12:00, and sunset is at 18:00. *Do not use A.M. or P.M. in the above equation; use a 24 hour clock only.* If the Sun, planet, or Moon is not near the celestial equator, the above equation may be off by more than an hour. The farther away one or both objects are from the celestial equator, the larger the error. The value of the equation of time (the difference between local apparent solar time and local mean solar time) is another factor that can introduce error.

II. Tutorial

Logon to **SKYLAB2** and select program No. 6, "PLANETMATION." This program animates the motions of the planets in their orbits as seen from any distance from the Sun. When you initially call up this program, it presents a view of the solar system at a distance of 6.0 Astronomical Units (AU) from the Sun, looking towards the south ecliptic pole with an inclination of 60°. The planetary motions begin with today's date and time and proceed in steps of one day every 0.2 seconds (the delay time).

1. Type "D" to open the distance window and change the distance to 50 AU.
2. Change the inclination to 0° by typing "V" to open the "View-angle" window.
3. As soon as the animation begins, press "H" and the orbit of Halley's Comet will be drawn showing where the comet is today.
4. Press "N" to show the names of the planets.
5. Press the space bar to halt the motion.
   a. Now look at the screen. Notice how crowded together the inner planets are on this scale. The names of the inner planets may overlap one another.
   b. Note the peculiar eccentricity of Pluto's orbit. Sometimes it is closer to the Sun than Neptune. Is this true for today's date? Remember that this is a planar projection of the orbits of the major planets onto the plane of the Earth's orbit, i.e., onto the **plane of the ecliptic.** It does not show the fact that Pluto's orbit is inclined to the ecliptic plane by 17°. Furthermore, the nodes of Pluto's orbit are located in the diagram at points far from where it appears Pluto could collide with Neptune. In other words, if both planets were at a point where you see the two orbits crossing, a large vertical distance would still separate them. This is because Pluto would be far out of the plane of Neptune's orbit.

Exercise 15.0

6. Now press "D" and change the distance to 10 AU.

    a. If the names of the planets are in the way for the following exercise, pressing "N"

    will remove them. You can put them back anytime you need them.

    b. Allow the animation of the planetary motions to run and watch what is happening. Now and then stop the motion and see if you can estimate the elongation of each planet. **To do this, imagine a line drawn from wherever the Earth is to the Sun and another line drawn from the Earth to the planet in question. The angle between these two lines is the planet's elongation.** The direction of the angle is west if clockwise from the Sun toward the planet or east if counterclockwise from the Sun towards the planet.

III. Assignment

1. After you have practiced estimating elongations for several different dates, set the step size to 6 hours and the delay time to 0.8 seconds.
2. Set the date to about 7-25-1991 and the distance to 3.0 AU.
3. Set the inclination angle to zero.
   a. On some day not too long after this date in 1991, the planets Mercury and Venus will be at inferior conjunction nearly at the same time. Start the motion and keep watching these two planets until you see them line up along a line between the Earth and the Sun. Press the space bar to stop the motion when you think this event has occurred.
   b. Rerun the motion backward several days and repeat until you are sure you have determined the correct date.
4. Record this date as No. 3 on the answer sheet and obtain a printout of the screen (#1).

5. Now set the date to your birthday of the current year, the time to 21:00, the distance to 3.5 AU, and the inclination to 0°. Do not use the date you obtained for question No. 4. Remove the names of the planets if you have them present. Obtain a printout of the screen. (This is printout #2)
6. Keep the same date and time but change only the distance to 40 AU. Make sure the orbit for Halley's Comets is included on the chart. Now get a printout of the screen. (#3)

    Proceed to analyze printouts #2 and #3 using your manual. You will no longer need the computer.

7. In the diagram on the first page of this exercise, use your protractor and measure the elongations for the two planetary positions marked A and B. Record these values on the answer sheet as 1 and 2; don't forget the direction.

8. Carefully study printout #1 and note the relative positions of the Sun, Earth, and the planets Mercury and Venus. Draw the zero-degree elongation line on the chart and label it as 0° where it meets the edge of the chart. Answer the following on the answer page:
   a. What is the elongation of Mercury and Venus on this date? (Nos. 4 & 5 on the answer page)
   b. What is the name for this planetary configuration or aspect? (No. 6 on the answer page)
   c. To what orbital class of planets do Mercury and Venus belong? (Answer Page, No. 7)

9. On printouts #2, draw a line from the center of the Earth to the center of the Sun and extend this line to the edge of the chart. Draw an arrow head at the latter position and label it 0°.
10. Now draw separate lines of sight from the Earth to Mercury, Venus and Mars. Continue

these lines beyond the planet as needed.

11. Use a protractor to measure the elongations of each planet and record the values on the answer sheet as No. 8. Be sure to label the angle as east or west.

12. Draw a bold arc between the two lines of sight defining each elongation angle at a position sufficiently far from the Earth so that you will be able to write the elongation and its direction along this arc along with an identification of the planet. See the chart at the end of the exercise to see how this is to be done. Also draw an arrowhead at the end of the arc where it touches the line of sight to the planet to indicate the sense of direction of the elongation. **Your charts should be annotated in the same way as the sample charts at the end of this exercise.**

13. Now you will need to establish the zero degree elongation line on chart #3 so that the elongations for the outer planets may be determined. This will be difficult, since at 40 AU the inner planets are located very close together and the location of the Earth will not be evident. However, we can use printout #2 to assist you in this matter.
    a. On printout #2, measure the distance between the intersection of the $0°$ elongation line with the boundary of the chart and a convenient corner of the boundary lines.
    b. On the 40 AU chart measure this same distance from the analogous corner of the chart and make a mark.
    c. Draw a line from the center of the Sun to this mark and make an arrowhead, which is to be labeled $0°$. You have now established the zero degree line on printout #3.

14. Now use printout #3 and repeat steps 9 through 12 for the planets Jupiter through Pluto, and Halley's Comet. Record the elongations in the blank lines for No. 9 on the answer sheet.

15. Use the value of the elongation you have determined for Venus on printout #2 and the equation

$$T_P = T_\odot - T_E,$$

which was explained in the introduction, to compute the time Venus will rise. Do this calculation and show the details on the answer page as No. 10.

16. Similarly, compute the time Mars will set. Do this as No. 11 on the answer page.

17. Now compute and show the details for what time Saturn rises as No. 12..

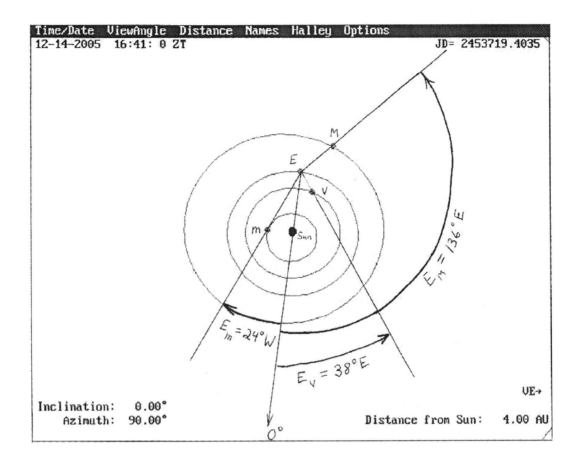

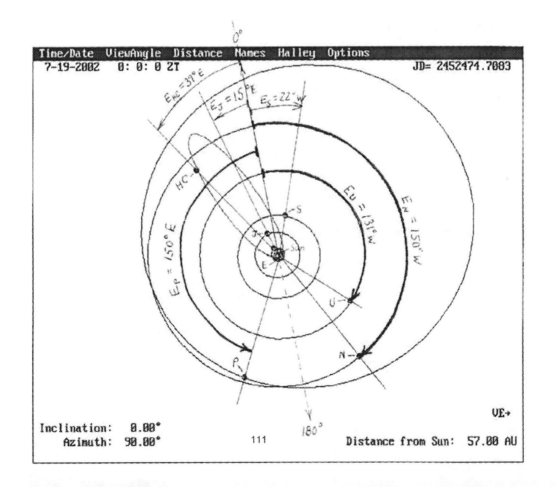

EXERCISE 15.0 ANSWER PAGE

Planetary Orbits and Configurations

1. Elongation of A from diagram in part I of Manual: .... _____

2. Elongation of B from diagram in part I of Manual: .... _____

3. Date of elongation: _____

4. Elongation of Mercury: .... _____ .

5. Elongation of Venus: _____

6. Configuration or Aspect name: _____

7. Orbital class for Mercury and Venus: .... _____

8. Mercury: _____ Venus: _____ Mars: _____

9. Jupiter: _____ Saturn: _____ Uranus: _____

    Neptune: _____ Pluto: _____ Halley's Comet _____

10. Calculation of the time Venus rises:

    a. Elongation of Venus in degrees: _____

    b. Value of T_E for Venus in hours and minutes with proper algebraic sign: _____

    c. Value of $T_\odot$ for Sun: _____

    d. $T_P = T_\odot - T_E$ = _____

11. Calculation of the time Mars sets:

    a. Elongation of Mars in degrees: _____

    b. Value of T_E for Mars in hours and minutes with proper algebraic sign: _____

    c. Value of $T_\odot$ for Sun: _____

    d. $T_P = T_\odot - T_E$ = _____

12. Calculation of the time Saturn rises:

    a. Elongation of Saturn in degrees: _____

    b, Value of T_E for Saturn in hours and minutes with proper algebraic sign: _____

    c. Value of $T_\odot$ for Sun: _____

    d. $T_P = T_\odot - T_E$ = _____

End

Exercise 15.1

Orbital Motion of a Comet

1. Logon to **Skylab2** and select the program "Planetmation." From the menu bar, select "Viewangle." Then set the "Inclination" to 0.0° and the "Azimuth" to 72°. Now set the distance to 29 AU.

2. Type "H" to plot the orbit of Halley's comet.

3. Under the options menu set the step to 5 days.

4. With the help of the right and left cursor keys, run the animation to find when Halley's comet is at the next aphelion and record the date and year below. You may expect an error of 2 or more months. **Obtain a hardcopy** of the screen image showing your result.

   Month: _____   Day: _____   Year: _____

5. Now let the program run until you find the date and year when the comet will be at what you judge to be the end of the minor axis of the orbit (this is just inside the orbit of Uranus). **Get a hardcopy** and record the date below:

   Month: _____   Day: _____   Year: _____

6. To determine the date of perihelion, reduce the step size to I day to make a more accurate determination. Also, zoom in to about 4AU, then search for the date and year when the comet will next be at perihelion and record below. **Obtain a hardcopy** of the screen after you have made your determination.

   Month: _____   Day: _____   Year: _____

The following analysis is to be done at home or in the lab room according to your instructor's directions.

7. Compute how many years, and decimal parts thereof, it took the comet to move from aphelion to the end of its minor axis. See part D of the on-line document "Time" on how to do this. Record the result below:

   Length of time: .... _____

8. How many years, and decimal parts thereof, did it take the comet to move from the end of its minor axis to the next perihelion? Record below:

   Length of time: .... _____

9. Compare the answers 7 and 8. What planetary law have you just verified?

   Answer: _____ .

Exercise 16.0

APPARENT PLANETARY MOTIONS
AND ASPECTS

I. Introduction

It is expected that Ex. 15.0 has been completed before attempting this exercise, since many of the definitions and concepts developed there will be needed here. Recall that the planets revolve around the sun in almost concentric orbits that lie nearly in the same plane as the Earth's orbit, with the exception of Pluto. Hence, in the sky, the planets are always to be found near the ecliptic, but Pluto can be as much as $17°$ off the ecliptic. Recall also that the angular distance of a planet from the Sun, as measured E/W along the ecliptic, is called elongation. Furthermore, there is a simple relation between a planet's elongation and the approximate time it will rise, make UT, or set. This is:

$$T_P = T_\odot - T_E$$

The meanings of the symbols in the above equation are as follows:

T_P = Local Time when a planet will rise, make upper transit, etc.
$T_\odot$ = Local Time for corresponding solar event: rise, set, etc.
T_E = Planetary elongation in time units.

The above equation works best when the planet and the Sun are both near the celestial equator. We can then assume that sunrise is 06:00, upper transit (UT) for the Sun is 12:00, and sunset is at 18:00. *Do not use A.M. or P.M. in the above equation; use a 24 hour clock only.* If the Sun, planet, or Moon is not near the celestial equator, the above equation may be off by more than an hour. The farther away one or both objects are from the celestial equator, the larger the error. The equation of time is another factor that can introduce error. In this exercise, you will be studying how elongation is represented on a rectangular chart of the celestial sphere.

II. Tutorial

Logon to **SKYLAB2** and select program "SKYMATION." A rectangular chart will then be drawn that represents the entire celestial sphere. An example is provided at the end of this exercise. The ecliptic appears as a wavy red curve. As soon as the chart is displayed, an animation will begin that shows the changing positions of the Sun, Moon, and planets in one day steps for the equatorial frame of reference. The positions of the planets, the Sun, and the Moon are indicated by small circles that are letter coded. The key to this code can be viewed as a window by typing "S" for symbols. Watch the animation run for a while to see what is happening and how the elongations of the Moon and planets change from day to day and then answer question 1 in Section III.

Note the vertical blue line that is slowly moving eastward each day. This is the LCM. Remember that the sidereal time is indicated by the hour circle of RA coincident with the LCM. Since the screen is being displayed for the same ZT on successive days but the sidereal clock runs faster than the mean solar clock, the motion of the LCM indicates the daily gain of the sidereal clock on the solar clock. Answer question 2 in Section III.

Now change the step size to 3 hours and delay factor to 0.8 second. This will enable you to see details happening over each day. Note the planets hardly move at all in three hours, but the Moon's motion is noticeable. The large jumps in the position of the LCM are the result of seeing where it is relative to the stars every 3 hours and thereby indicating the sidereal time for the

Exercise 16.0

corresponding ZT indicated at the top of the screen. This eastward motion of the LCM is an alternative way of representing diurnal motion of the celestial sphere westward relative to the LCM. Recall that the parallels of declination are the diurnal circles.

III. ASSIGNMENT

Record your answers to the following on the answer page for this exercise.

1. Which object has the largest day to day displacement relative to the stars and in what general direction, E or W?
2. In the Skymation animation, how much does the LCM move, in minutes, relative to the stars in one day and it what direction? To do this, set the step size to exactly one day and let the animation run so that the LCM moves some definite amount of RA in a given number of days.

Note that the Sun is always on the ecliptic and moves eastward from day to day.

3. How many degrees does it move each day on the average and in what direction?

Note that as the moon traverses its orbit it is sometimes north of the ecliptic and sometimes south of the ecliptic.

4. Why is this?

Reset the date to today's before continuing the motion. Note that the planets move along curves that are nearly coincident with the ecliptic. These curves are the projections of the planetary orbits onto the plane of the sky. The fact that the planets move along curves that are nearly coincident with the ecliptic expresses the fact that the planetary orbits lie nearly in the plane of the Earth's orbit, which is the same as the ecliptic plane.

5. Which planet has its orbit inclined the most to the ecliptic plane?
6. Estimate how far this planet is currently from the ecliptic?

Now concentrate your attention on the motion of Mercury? Note that this planet appears to oscillate east and west of the sun by a limited angular distance. Reset the date to about a month before today's and run the animation at high speed using the right cursor key to determine when Mercury is approximately at its next greatest elongation after today's date. If this occurs close to today's date, you may need to start further back from today's date. After you have the approximate date, run the animation at a slower rate to make a more accurate determination. **Warning: If the planet attained a greatest elongation just shortly before today's date, the next elongation after today's date won't occur until the planet moves to the other side of the Sun.**

7. Is this east or west of the sun? Circle which on the answer sheet and record the date when the next greatest elongation after today happens.
8. Reset the date to the current one and repeat for Venus. Record the direction and date of its next greatest elongation.

Sometimes the superior planets stop moving eastward (prograde) and reverse direction to move westward (retrograde) for a while. Then they reverse direction again and move prograde, thereby forming a loop in the sky. To see this, reset the date to Oct. 1, 1992 and select to trail Mars. Allow the motion to run and watch the trail.

9. Determine the date that Mars halts its eastern motion and begins to move westward. You can use the left arrow key to reverse the motion and make several determinations of this date, then record the average.

10. Estimate the elongation of Mars on this date.

11. What is the explanation for this peculiar behavior of the superior planets? It would be helpful to run the program **Planetmation** and watch the motion of the Earth and Mars in their orbits over this time interval.

Reset the date to that assigned to you or your birthday (not Oct. 1, 1992) and stop the animation; what time it is doesn't matter. Obtain a printout of the screen. This printout will be analyzed later.

Now watch the diurnal motion of the planets in the horizon system as follows: Type "C" to open the coordinates menu and select "Horizon". Pan up by 15 degrees then zoom out by a factor of 2. Allow the animation to run and watch the planets move along their diurnal circles relative to the horizon and LCM. The latter is fixed at azimuth 180°. Notice that the planets rise from the east, ascend to upper transit on the LCM, and then descend to set in the west. If you wish you may add a few stars under options but use a magnitude cut-off no larger than three, otherwise things will get too confusing. From the diurnal motion you just observed, answer the following:

12. What planets will be visible in the evening sky after the sun sets.

13. What planets will be visible in the morning sky just before sunrise?

Reset to the date given above and stop the animation when Jupiter sets (altitude = 0^0).

14. Record the ZT Jupiter sets on the answer sheet.

15. Now do the same for Saturn on the same day and record the ZT for setting.

Analysis of Printout

Use a flexible ruler to measure along the ecliptic the 180° angular distance between the vernal and autumnal equinoxes in centimeters. Then determine the elongation chart scale along the ecliptic of degrees per cm.

16. Now use the flexible ruler and elongation chart scale to determine the elongation of Saturn. Draw and label this angle on your chart as shown on the sample chart at the end of this exercise.

17. Convert the elongation in degrees to time units, then compute what time Saturn should set, using the equation in part I. Show your calculation on the answer sheet.

18. Now measure the elongation of Jupiter and record on the answer sheet. Draw and label this angle on your chart as you did for Saturn.

19. Just as you did for Saturn, compute what time Jupiter will set.

Compare these values with the values you computed for questions 14 and 15. Remember that if the planet or the Sun, or both, are not near the CE, your computed value using the equation $T_P = T_\odot - T_E$ will be different from the actual value, which are closer to the answers for 14 and 15.

20. For which planet do your calculations agree closer to the actual value?

21. What is different about the positions of the two planets in the equatorial system that may explain why one is more accurate than the other.

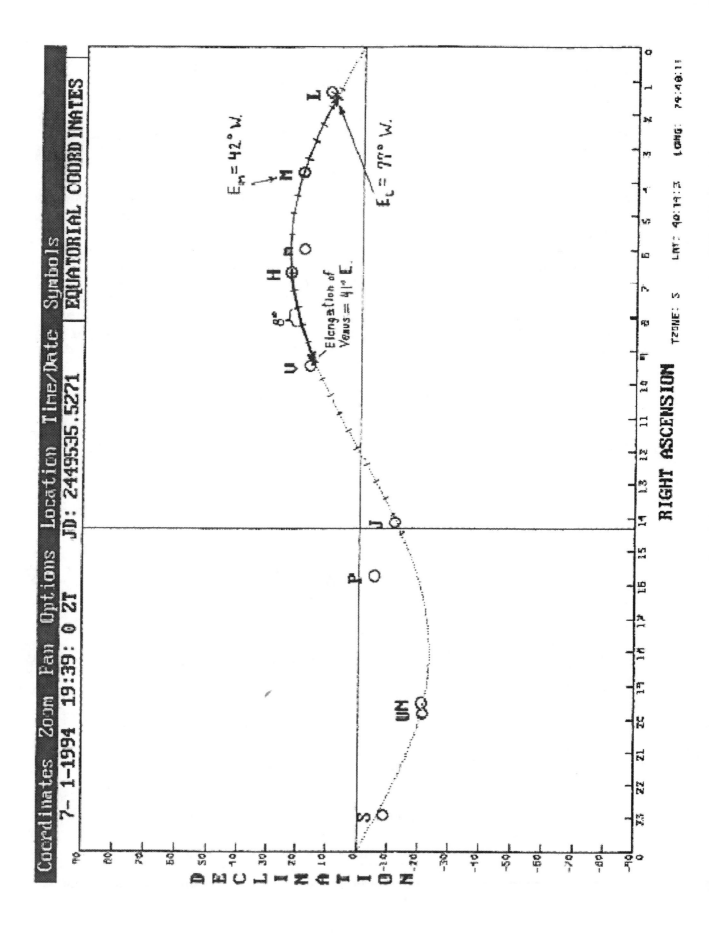

EXERCISE 16.0 ANSWER PAGE

APPARENT PLANETARY MOTIONS AND ASPECTS

1. Object with largest daily motion: _____ Direction_____.

2. Amount of LCM motion in minutes per day: _____ Direction_____.

3. Sun's motion per day: _____.

4. Why Moon moves N/S of ecliptic: _____

   _____.

5. Planet with most inclined orbit is _____.

6. Distance of above planet from ecliptic is _____.

7. Date Mercury is next at greatest E / W (circle which) elongation is_____.

8. Date Venus is next at greatest E / W (circle which) elongation is _____.

9. Date Mars halts prograde motion: _____.

10. Elongation of Mars on above date: _____.

11. Explanation for retrograde motion: _____

    _____

    _____.

12. Planets visible in evening sky: _____

13. Planets visible in morning sky: _____

14. Time Jupiter sets: _____.

15. Time Saturn sets: _____.

16. Elongation of Saturn in degrees_____.

17. Time Saturn sets: _____. Show calculation details below:

18. Elongation of Jupiter in degrees:_____.

19. Time Jupiter sets: _____. Show calculation details below:

20. Planet for which calculations agree better: _____.

21. Explanation for disagreement:

Exercise 16.1

PLANETARY EPHEMERIDES

This exercise is meant to provide a chart of the sky and data to assist one in observing the planets for a particular date and time. One needs to review Ex. 10 before proceeding.

1. Logon to **Skylab2** and run the program "SKYMATION." Select a date and time that you want to observe the planets. Call for a "grid" and "plot star" under Options. Get a printout of this chart.

2. Refer to the directions in Exercise 10.0 for locating and drawing the celestial horizon on the printout. Identify and label the upper local celestial meridian as ULCM. Locate the position of the lower local celestial meridian then draw it as a dashed vertical line from the top of the chart to the bottom and label it as LLCM. Locate and label the N, S, E, and W points of the celestial horizon. Now connect these points with a smooth, wavy curve using a colored pencil and label as the horizon.

3. Determine the chart scale for converting hour angle (HA) in cm to HA in hours and minutes. Refer back to Exercise 4.0 if you have forgotten bow to do this. Record your measurements and the results of your calculation below:

   Measurement: _____ cm = _____ hours of RA.

   Chart Scale: _____(hours/cm).

4. Select a planet that is above the horizon that you would like to observe and record below. Draw a horizontal line from the center of the planet to the western horizon. Measure in cm to the second decimal place the length of this line and record below. Multiply this by the above chart scale to convert cm into hours and decimal parts thereof. Now convert the decimal part of the hours to minutes and record below. This is the amount of time until the planet sets.

   Planet to be observed: _____. Distance from western horizon in cm: _____ .

   Amount of time until planet sets in hours and minutes: _____.

5. Add the amount of time until the planet sets to the current zone time (ZT) at the top of the chart and record the result below. It should now be possible for you to determine whether or not you will have time to observe this planet if you start your observations at the zone time for which the chart was generated.

   Zone Time the planet sets: _____.

6. Telescopic observations of the planets are best when the planet is within a few hours of upper transit. Examine your chart and list below the planets that are near UT:

   Planets near UT: _____.

7. If a planet is close to the horizon, it can not be observed very well. List below the planets that are within 0.5 hours of either the eastern or western horizon.

   Planets close to the horizon: _____.

Exercise 17.0

STELLAR PARALLAX AND DISTANCE

I. Stellar Parallax

Parallax is defined to be the angular displacement of an object when viewed from two different positions that are located along a line perpendicular to one of the lines of sight. The idea of detecting the revolution of the Earth in its orbit around the Sun, by measuring the parallactic displacements that would result for nearby stars, goes back to Aristotle's time (about 350 BC). However, stellar parallaxes were not observed because the parallax of even the closest star is too small to be detected without a telescope. It took until 1837 AD for the first stellar parallax to be successfully measured. This was done independently by Bessel in Germany and Struve in Russia. The geometry for determining the parallaxes of the stars, and, thereby, calculating their distances is illustrated in the diagram below. In this diagram, the size of the Earth's orbit relative to the distance of the nearby star is greatly exaggerated for clarity.

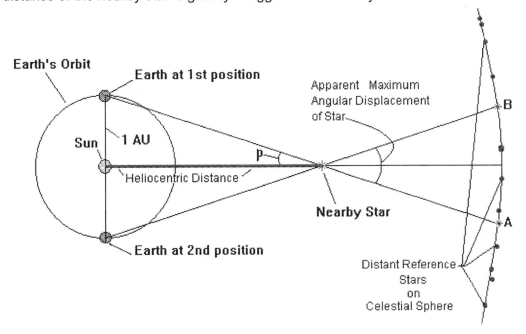

As the Earth moves in orbit around the Sun, a nearby star appears to change its position on the celestial sphere with respect to much more distant stars. Very distant stars have negligible parallactic displacements and, therefore, serve as reference points for measuring the changing position of the star whose parallax we want to determine. When the Earth is at the 1st position in its orbit, the nearby star is seen on the celestial sphere at position A. Six months later, when the Earth has moved to the second position, the nearby star now is seen to be at position B on the celestial sphere. For any other position of the Earth in its orbit, the nearby star would be seen to have a position somewhere between these two extreme positions. Hence, in six months a star suffers its maximum angular displacement in the sky as a result of the Earth's revolution. Half of this angle is the parallax, p.

In the above diagram, the parallactic triangle consists of the radius of the Earth's orbit, the heliocentric distance of the star, and the angle p. Since this is a right triangle, once p is measured, the heliocentric distance of the star can be calculated using trigonometry. We start by defining a value called the tangent of the angle p, or tan p, as:

$$\text{tan p = (side opposite p) / (side adjacent to p)}$$

This relation is valid for any of the angles in a right triangle. For the parallactic angle p shown in the above diagram, the side opposite p is the radius of the Earth's orbit, which is 1 AU. The side adjacent is the heliocentric distance of the star, D. We may write the above relation as:

$$\text{tan p = 1 AU / D.}$$

It follows then that D = 1 AU / tan p.

Even for the closest neighboring stars of the Sun, the heliocentric distances are at least 200 thousand times greater than the radius of the Earth's orbit. Hence, parallaxes for these stars are very small fractions of a degree. A general rule is:

The more distant the star, the smaller is its parallax.

The sun's nearest neighbor in space is the triple star-system called Alpha Centauri. This system has a parallax of 0.750 arcseconds, which corresponds to a distance of approximately 4 light years. All other stars have parallaxes smaller than this.

Astronomers prefer to express stellar distances in parsecs (pc), where:

1 parsec corresponds to the heliocentric distance in
a parallactic triangle where p is equal to 1 arcsecond.

The tangent of 1 arcsecond, or 0.000278 degrees, is 4.8×10^{-6}. Substituting this value into the expression D = 1 AU / tan p, we get that D = 206,265 au. This means:

1 parsec must be 206,265 AU, or 3.26 light years.

But remember, there is no star this close to the Sun and even Alpha Centauri is more than 1 pc away. Hence, all stars have a parallax less than 1 arcsecond.

When we express the heliocentric distance D in parsecs and p is always expressed in arcseconds, then the equation D = 1 AU / tan p simplifies to

$$\text{D = 1/p.}$$

For example, if a star were found to display a parallax of 0.25 arcseconds, its heliocentric distance would be D = 1/0.25 = 4 parsecs.

II. Measurement of Stellar Parallax

The two diagrams below are simulated photographs of the star field surrounding the star labeled as C, taken 6 months apart. The linear distance between the two stars marked A and B on both photographs is known to be 4.00 arcseconds. This establishes the chart scale for converting cm into arcseconds.

Now we devise a way to measure the parallax of star C and then calculate its distance. This may be accomplished by measuring the position of star C relative to the stars on chart 2 and then plot this same relative position on chart 1. Remember that every star in the two photos may be assumed to be in the same position except for star C. One cannot make measurements of the position of star C relative to the edges of the charts. This is because the edges of the charts (photographs) are not necessarily aligned with the star field exactly the same way in each case.

Exercise 17.0

However, transferring the position of star C on chart 2 to the same relative position on chart 1 can be accomplished as follows:

1. Draw a straight line from star A to star B on both charts. This line establishes an x-axis with star A at the origin, that is, at x= 0.00.

2. Measure the distance between the stars A and B in cm with a precision of 2 decimal places and record on the answer sheet. From this measurement, you will be able to compute the chart scale giving the number of arcseconds per centimeter.

3. Take a protractor and use the flat edge to draw a line perpendicular to the x-axis on chart 2 and through the star C. This line becomes the y-axis. To do this correctly, the mark on the protractor for 90° should be aligned with the x-axis, that is, the line through stars A and B. See the diagram on the answer page.

4. Measure the distance on chart 2 from star A to the y-axis, that is, to the point of intersection with the perpendicular line through star C. Record this on the answer page as x. As always, your precision should be 2 decimal places.

5. Measure the distance of star C along the y-axis from the x-axis and record on the answer page as y. With the two measurements x and y, it should be possible to establish the location of star C on chart 1. This must be done with great precision, measuring to the hundredth of a centimeter, or you will incur a large error.

6. On chart 1, establish the y-axis perpendicular to the x-axis using the value of x from the answer page and your protractor, the same way you did on chart 2.

7. Now use the y value for star C to locate this star on chart 1.

8. Draw a fine line between the two different positions of star C on chart 1, then measure very precisely this distance and record this on the answer page.

9. You should realize that the above distance, when multiplied by the chart scale you found in step 2, is the value of TAAD in arcseconds. Do this and record the result on the answer page.

10. Take half of TAAD and this is the parallax.

11. Compute the heliocentric distance of the star.

III. Simulated Images of a Star Field

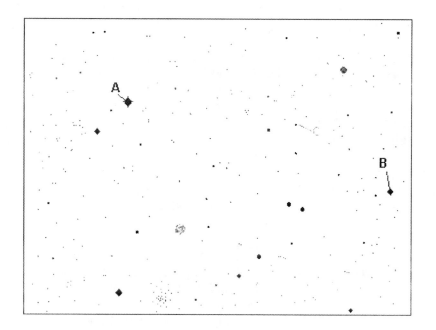

CHART 1

CHART 2

Stellar Parallax Answer Page

Measured distance between stars A and B in cm to 2 decimal places: _____ = 4.00"

Computed chart scale from above data (divide arcseconds by cm): _____ ("/cm)

Measured x and y coordinates of Star C on Chart 2: x = _____ cm, y = _____ cm.

From Chart 1:

Measured total annual displacement of Star C in cm = ... _____ cm.

Total annual angular displacement (TAAD) in arcseconds = ... _____ .

Parallax, p, of Star C in arcseconds (1/2 of TAAD) = ……………………….._____ .

Heliocentric distance of Star C in parsecs (HD = 1/p) = ……………………… _____ pc.

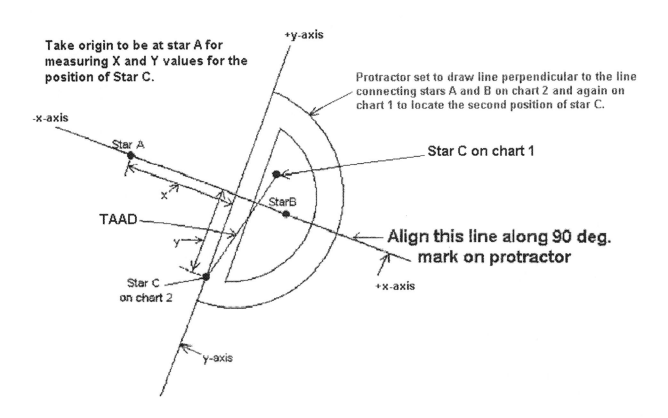

Take origin to be at star A for measuring X and Y values for the position of Star C.

Protractor set to draw line perpendicular to the line connecting stars A and B on chart 2 and again on chart 1 to locate the second position of star C.

+y-axis

-x-axis

Star A

Star C on chart 1

StarB

TAAD

Align this line along 90 deg. mark on protractor

+x-axis

Star C on chart 2

x

y

y-axis

Exercise 17.1

STELLAR MOTIONS

1. Space Motion

Stars are moving in orbit around the center of the Galaxy. Near the Sun, there are slight deviations of each star's motion from that of its neighbors. The difference between the Sun's motion and another star's motion is observed to be what is called a star's "space motion". The space motion, S, is the vector sum of what is called the tangential velocity of a star V_T and its radial velocity V_R. See the diagram below:

The radial velocity may be determined independently of the tangential velocity by measuring the Doppler Effect in a star's spectrum. This we shall address later, after we learn about the Doppler Effect and learn some spectroscopy.

The tangential velocity may be determined if the distance of the star is known and something called the "proper motion" of the star can be measured. **Proper motion is the annual angular rate of motion of a star across the line of sight to the star.** It is represented by the lower case Greek letter μ, and is expressed in arcseconds per year. The proper motion may be converted to the tangential velocity of the star, if the distance of the star is determined. In the

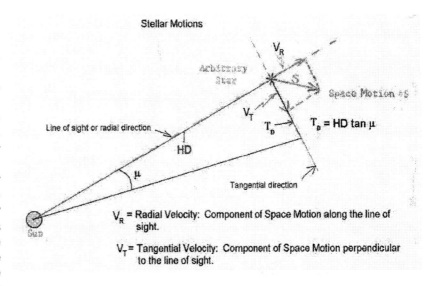

Stellar Motions

V_R = Radial Velocity: Component of Space Motion along the line of sight.

V_T = Tangential Velocity: Component of Space Motion perpendicular to the line of sight.

diagram, the side of the triangle that is marked HD is the heliocentric distance of the star and the side labeled T_D is the distance the star moves in one year traveling with velocity V_T. That is, the star appears to move through the angle μ in one year.

Determining the space motion of a star is complicated by the orbital motion of the Earth around the Sun and the Sun's motion in orbit about the center the galaxy. First consider the effects of the Earth's orbital motion, which is reflected in a star's proper motion. Essentially the Earth's orbital motion superposes an apparent oscillation on the star's proper motion. Once this is understood, an analysis of the observed motion of a star will yield both the distance of the star and the star's tangential velocity.

2. Proper Motions

Exactly how the parallactic displacement of star affects the observed motion of a star depends on the angular distance of the star above or below the plane of the Earth's orbit. If the star is located in the plane of the Earth's orbit and the star had no proper motion (this does not actually happen), it would appear to move back and forth along a straight line. This is the case shown in the diagram in Exercise 17.0 showing parallax. So in that exercise, we have assumed the star has no proper motion.

If the star were above or below the plane of the Earth's orbit, the star would appear to move around a very small ellipse on the celestial sphere. The semi-major axis of the ellipse in arcseconds would be the parallax of the star.

The greater the angle between the plane of the Earth's orbit and the position of the star, the more circular the parallactic ellipse would look. If the star were 90° above the plane of the Earth's orbit it would be at the north ecliptic pole and the parallactic ellipse would actually be a circle. The radius of this circle in arcseconds would be the parallax of the star.

If the star has a proper motion, this would result in the motion of the parallactic ellipse on the celestial sphere, along the direction of the proper motion.

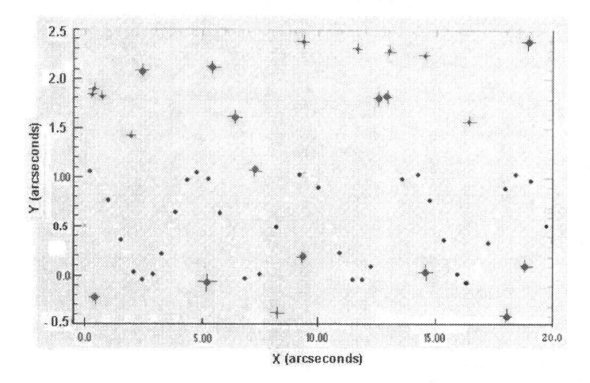

The diagram above displays measured positions (black dots) of a star on the celestial sphere in arcseconds relative to other stars around it (dots with crosses). The displacement of the parallactic ellipse due to the proper motion of the star results in a wave, which is revealed by drawing a curve among the data points that is the best fit. When drawing the best fit wave amongst the data points, allow for random errors in the positional measurement. Do not just connect the dots. The wave should be symmetrical and have the same amplitude everywhere along its length.

The amount of time it takes to make one complete cycle in the wave is one year.

The semi-amplitude of the wave is the parallax and the wavelength of the wave in arcseconds is the proper motion. A better result for the parallax is obtained if one measures the amplitude of the wave in several places, takes an average and then divide the average by 2 to get the semi-amplitude, which is the parallax.

To measure the amplitude or semi-amplitude of the wave in arcseconds you will need to find the vertical chart scale in arcseconds per cm. This is different than the horizontal chart scale, which is to be used to measure the wavelength in arcseconds. Now determine the vertical and horizontal chart scales for the above chart and record your data on the answer page. Then follow the other steps on the answer page to ultimately calculate the distance and tangential velocity of the star.

ANSWER PAGE FOR EXERCISE 17.1

1. First make the necessary measurements to determine the horizontal and vertical chart scales in ("/cm). Measure the largest distances possible, between fiducial points, along the sides of the chart to get the best results. Be careful, the edges of the charts may not always have designated fiducial values of the coordinates Record your measurements and do the calculations here:

   Distance along y-axis in cm: _____   Chart scale for y-axis _____ ("/cm)

   Distance along x-axis in cm: _____   Chart scale for x-axis _____ ("/cm)

2. Draw a smooth, symmetrical curve among the data points that is the best fit. Make several measurements of the amplitude of the wave (from peak to trough) in cm at several different places along the wave, take an average, and record your answer below. Multiply this by the vertical chart scale to convert cm to arcseconds and record on the next line. Half of this (the semi-amplitude) is the parallax of the star. Record this on the next line.

   Ave. amplitude in cm. _____.   Ave. amplitude in arcsecs. _____.

   Parallax in arcseconds: _____.

3. Calculate the distance of the star as explained in Ex. 17.0 and record here: HD = _____ (pc).

4. Measure the wavelength of the wave in cm at several places along the wave (peak to peak), take an average and record your answer below. Multiply this by the horizontal chart scale and record your results. This is the proper motion of the star in arcseconds per year:

   Proper Motion wavelength in cm: _____.   Proper motion, μ, in arcseconds/year: _____ .

5. The actual distance that the star has moved through space, perpendicular to the line of sight, in one year is T_D and may be calculated from:

$$T_D = HD \tan \mu$$

   But to find $\tan \mu$ with your calculator, the proper motion must be converted to degrees by dividing μ by 3600 arcseconds per degree. Record this value here with 3 significant figures: .... _____(deg./yr).

6. Then use your calculator to find $\tan \mu$. Record this value here (express in powers of ten): _____.

7. Multiply this by HD to get T_D and record here: ...._____ (pc/yr.).
   This is actually the tangential velocity of the star in parsecs per year.

8. Now calculate the number of seconds in a year and record here:......................... _____ (sec/yr).
   Divide the answer in 7 by the number of seconds in a year and this is the tangential velocity of the star in parsecs per second.

   T_D in pc/sec: _____.

   If we multiply the last answer in 8, T_D, by the number of kilometers in a parsec (you should be able to calculate what this is), we obtain the tangential velocity of the star in km/sec. First use the data given in Exercise 17.0 to help you calculate the number of kilometers in a parsec and record this as item 9:

9. No. of kilometers in a parsec: ...._____ (km/pc).

   Now multiply the value of TD in 8 by the value in 9:

10. Tangential velocity of star in km/sec.: ...._____(km/sec).

Exercise 18.0

DETERMINING APPARENT MAGNITUDES

I. Introduction

The ancient Greek, Hipparchus, circa 150 BC, devised what is now called the magnitude system for expressing apparent stellar brightness.

Brightness: the amount of radiant or light energy received per second from a light source.

Apparent brightness: The brightness of an object as viewed from the Earth.

Hipparchus divided all the stars visible to his unaided eye into 6 classes of apparent brightness. He identified a number of stars which he considered were the brightest that could be seen and assigned to these, the number 1. To the faintest stars that he could recognize he assigned the number 6. To the stars in between these two extreme cases he assigned the numbers 2 through 5. We now call these numerical classes of brightness, magnitudes (m).

After the invention of the telescope, stars fainter than $m = 6$ could be seen, so these were assigned magnitude numbers > 6, e.g. $m = 8$. With today's technology, stars can be detected down to the 28th magnitude or $m = 28$. In modern times, the magnitude system has been defined very precisely so that fractions of a magnitude may be assigned, e.g. $m = 8.34$. Furthermore, brightness can be measured objectively using instruments attached to a telescope rather than using the human eye.

In the modern magnitude system, a step or difference of 5 magnitudes ($\Delta m = 5$) has been defined to correspond to a brightness ratio of exactly 100. That is, we receive 100 times more light energy per second from a 3rd magnitude star than from an 8th magnitude star or we receive 100 times more light energy per second from a 5th magnitude star than from a 10th magnitude star. In each of the latter examples, the difference in magnitude is exactly 5.

For a step of exactly 1 magnitude ($\Delta m = 1.00$), the brightness ratio is the 5th root of 100 or 2.512. For two stars that have any arbitrary difference in magnitude, the brightness ratio is defined to be:

$$\text{Brightness Ratio} = 2.512^{\Delta m}$$

Near the beginning of the 20th century, astronomers decided that a group of faint stars near the north celestial pole would anchor the zero point of the modern magnitude system. This was accomplished by defining the average brightness of the stars in this group to be exactly $m = 6.000$. When this was done, the above relationship between brightness ratio and magnitude made some of the stars that Hipparchus had designated as 1st magnitude more than 100 times brighter than stars of the 6th magnitude. This necessitated introducing zero and negative magnitudes. For example, in the modern magnitude system, the apparent magnitude of the star Sirius is $m = -1.47$, whereas Hipparchus had called it a 1st magnitude star.

The modern magnitude system is applicable to any celestial body, including the Sun ($m = -27$), the Moon ($m = -12.5$ when full), the planets (Venus gets as bright as $m = -4.4$), comets, galaxies, etc. Interestingly, if the Sun were viewed from the outskirts of the solar system, it would appear to have a magnitude of -2, which is about the apparent magnitude of Jupiter. This emphasizes the fact that the apparent magnitude one determines for an object depends on the distance of the object from the observer.

The apparent magnitude of any object is defined to be:

$$m = C - 2.5 \log (b),$$

where C is a calibration constant that characterizes the instrumental system used for measuring the brightness b. The brightness b may be expressed in various units, even a relative number on some arbitrary scale, such as one to be used in this exercise. The calibration constant C is found by measuring values of b for many different stars that have magnitudes already defined in some system. Since m and b are then known for each star, we can solve the above equation for C in each case. One then computes an average value for C from all of the determinations. This is what you are going to do in this exercise.

The most widely accepted standard system of magnitudes is the **U, B, V, R, I** color magnitude system that was established by H. L. Johnson in the middle of the 20th century. These are magnitudes measured with filters that isolate ultraviolet (**U**), blue (**B**), yellow-green (**V**), red (**R**), and infrared (**I**) portions of the spectrum. There are two different ways to express such color magnitudes, either as $m_v = 3.23$, or V = 3.23.

On the following pages are photocopies of strip-chart recordings of relative brightness for several stars and the background readings for the sky near each star. These measurements were made using a photometric system consisting of an 8" diameter refracting telescope, a photoelectric photometer containing a 1P21 photomultiplier tube, and color filters that closely match those used by H. L. Johnson. The strip-chart recorder consists of a small motor that moves a long roll of graph paper from one reel to another at a precise rate so that time may be indicated on the chart. It also has a recording pen that constantly monitors the output of the photometric system. After a star is centered in the field of view of the telescope, a small window is opened to allow the star's light to enter the electronic photomultiplier tube. The tube responds to the light by generating an electric current proportional to the brightness of the light. This electric current is amplified and then causes the recording pen to deflect in proportion to the brightness of the star.

II. Assignment

Examine the attached charts. Notice that each page has brightness deflections for one star. The name of the star is written near one or more of the deflections. Each of the deflections is labeled with the filter used, and an amplifier setting. On the same page with the star readings are deflections for the brightness of the sky located near the star. The pen deflections are noisy due to several causes, but mainly atmospheric turbulence. One must imagine that the chatter or noise in the deflection is centered on some average value. It is this average value that you must determine. Each reading must be done to one decimal place precision. For example, look at the yellow or V deflection for ζ Hyd on the first chart. An estimate for the average value of this deflection may be 41.7. This value is not necessarily the correct value.

Now follow the following steps:

1. For a given star, estimate an average value for each deflection and also for the sky for each filter. Enter these values in Table 2 on the first two lines in the appropriate boxes for the filters.

2. Subtract the sky reading from the star reading for each filter and enter the net reading on the 3rd line in the appropriate boxes.

3. Enter the amplifier settings on the next line in the appropriate places. Be sure to account for the power of ten.

4. Multiply the net readings by the amplifier settings and record on the next line in the appropriate boxes for each filter. These are the values of b.

Exercise 18.0

5. Use your calculator to find the log of each of the above values and enter on the next line.

6. Repeat the above for each star.

7. Use the known value of V, B, or U as m for each of the standard stars from Table 1 and your value of log b for that star to calculate the value of C from **C = m + 2.5 log (b)**. Enter these values of C in the appropriate boxes in Table 3 for the appropriate column labeled V, B, or U. You can not do this for the star V834 Ori, or θ Hyd, because they are to be considered as stars with color magnitudes that are unknown at this point.

The values of C that you will get for the 3 different standard stars will be slightly different due to errors of measurement and many other factors. These errors can be reduced by taking a mean value for each filter.

8. For each column in Table 3, find the average or mean value of C and enter on the last line of the Table.

9. Now take the mean value of C in Table 3 for each filter and the corresponding values of log b for the stars V834 Ori and θ Hyd and use the magnitude equation (**m = C − 2.5 log (b)**) to compute values of V, B, and U for these two stars. Enter your computed values on the last line of Table 4 labeled "magnitudes."

Table 1

Color Magnitudes for Standard Stars

Star	V	B	U
ζ Hyd	3.10	4.11	4.91
ρ Hyd	4.37	4.32	4.27
ε Tau	3.53	4.54	5.41

EXERCISE 18.0

DETERMINING STELLAR MAGNITUDES

Table 2
Data from Charts for Standard Stars of Known Magnitudes

ζ Hyd				ρ Hyd			
Filters	V	B	U	Filters	V	B	U
Star Reading				Star Reading			
Sky Reading				Sky Reading			
Net Reading				Net Reading			
Amp. Setting				Amp. Setting			
b= NR x Amp. Set log b				b= NR x Amp. Set log b			
ε Tau							
Filters	V	B	U				
Star Reading							
Sky Reading							
Net Read							
Amp. Setting							
b= NR x Amp. Set log b							

Table 3
Values of Calibration Constants Calculated from C=m+2.5log(b)

Star	C_v	C_b	C_u
ζ Hyd			
ρ Hyd			
ε Tau			
Mean Value			

Table 4

Data for Stars of Unknown Magnitudes

V834 Ori			
Filters	V	B	U
Star Reading			
Sky Reading			
Net Reading			
Amp. Setting			
b = NR x Amp. Set			
log b			
magnitude			
θ Hyd			
Filters	V	B	U
Star Reading			
Sky Reading			
Net Read			
Amp. Setting			
b = NR x Amp. Set			
log b			
magnitude			

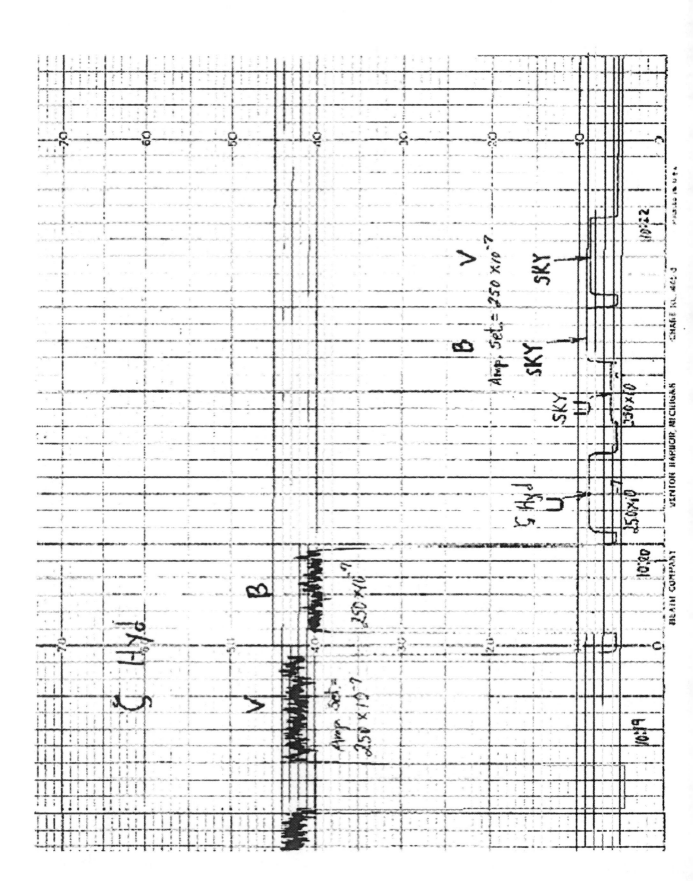

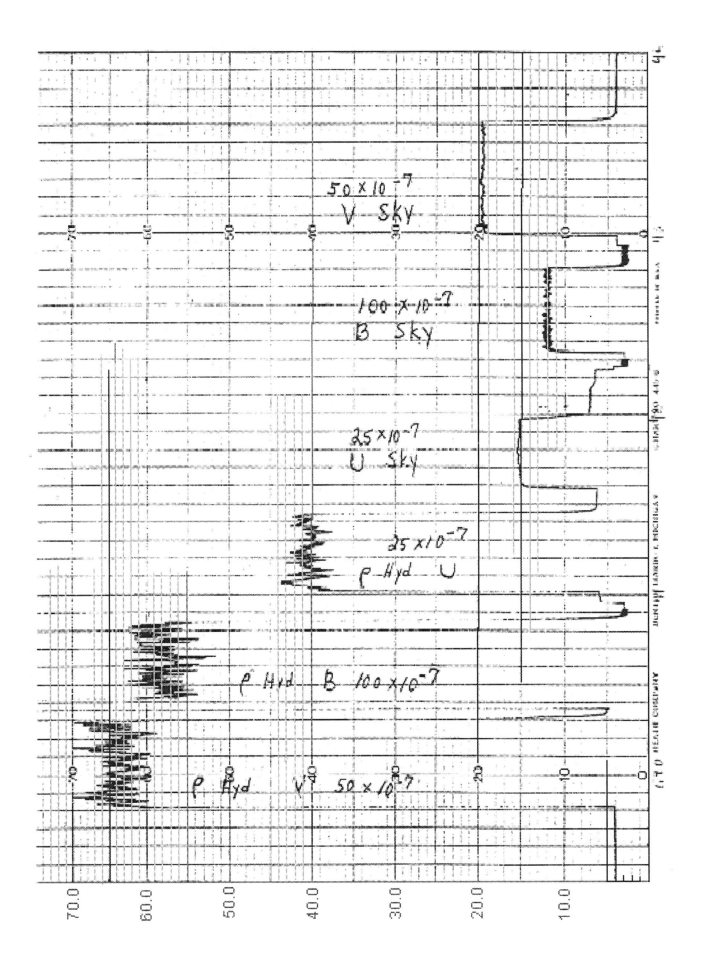

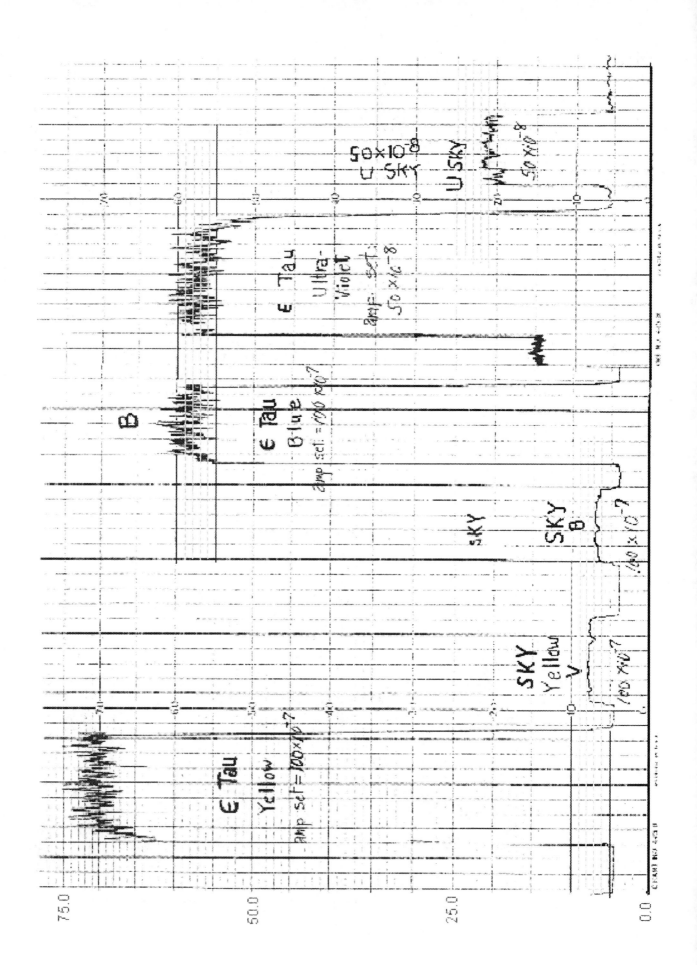

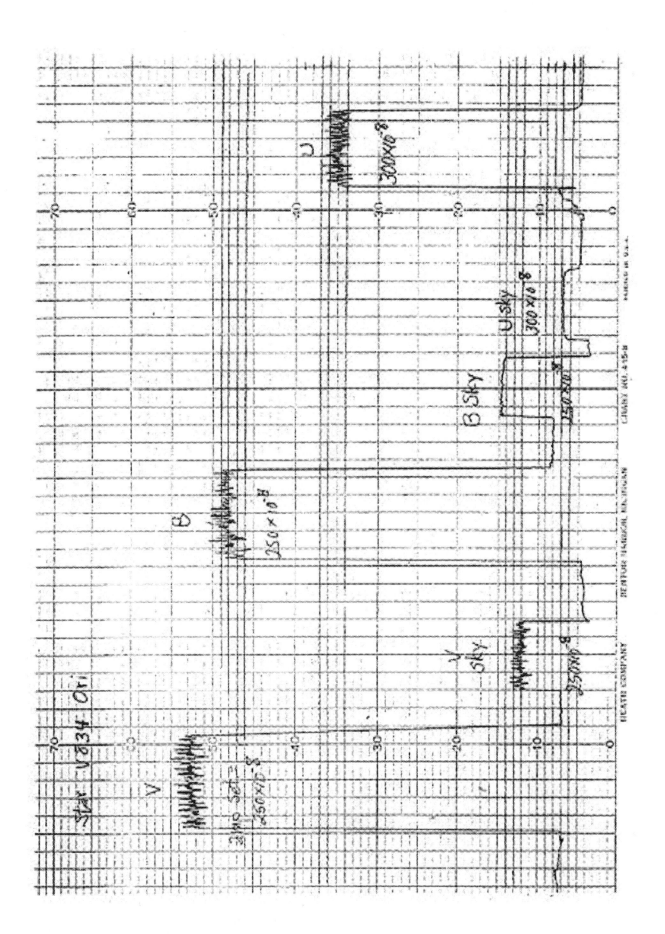

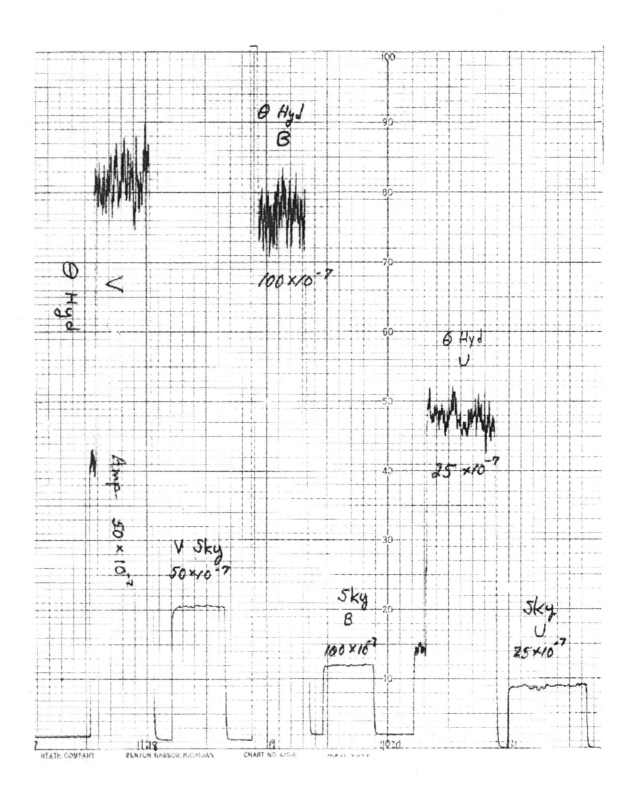

EXERCISE 18.5

LIGHT CURVE ANALYSIS OF AN ECLIPSING BINARY STAR SYSTEM

I. Binary Star Systems.

A binary star system is a gravitationally bound pair of stars revolving in orbit around a common barycenter or center of gravity. As the stars in a binary system revolve in orbit, they may eclipse one another as seen by an observer. When the stars are seen to be together in the plane of the sky, the stars are said to be in conjunction. The orbital phase is then either 0.0 or 0.5 for circular orbits. *The orbital phase is simply the decimal part of a complete orbital cycle.* Phase 0.50 means the stars have moved around half of their orbit since phase 0.00, the latter being designated as primary conjunction. See the diagram below.

At the conjunctions, one star may be partially or totally eclipsing the other, thereby reducing the observed brightness or flux of the system. Plotting the observed flux or brightness of the system versus orbital phase yields what is called the light curve of the system. By analyzing the light curve, much information about the stars can be learned.

Phase 0.00 is usually taken to be the middle of the eclipse of the brighter star. This is called primary eclipse. If the orbits are circular, the middle of the eclipse of the fainter star is phase 0.50. At what are called the quadrature phases (0.25 and 0.75), the stars are at their maximum separation as seen in the plane of the sky and the observed flux for the system will be a maximum. Furthermore, one star is moving towards us and the other away from us at the quadrature phases. Which star is moving towards and which is moving away is reversed at the other quadrature phase.

At phase 0.0, mid-eclipse is occurring for what shall be called star 1. Star 1 is called the primary. The star eclipsed at or near phase 0.5 shall be called star 2 or the secondary star. Therefore, the latter eclipse is called secondary eclipse. Secondary eclipse does not necessarily occur at phase 0.5, depending on whether the orbit is circular or elliptical. If the orbit is circular, then the middle of the secondary eclipse should be at phase 0.5. If not, the orbit is elliptical.

Primary and Secondary Conjunctions

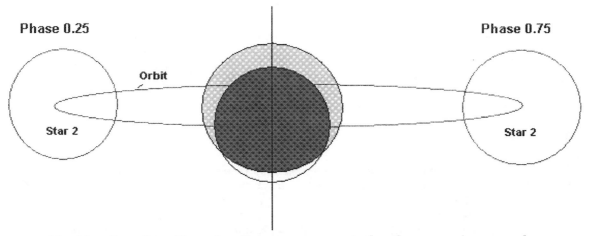

At mid-eclipse for either star, the same amount of surface area is covered, but not the same fractional area for each star

Notice in the above diagram, that the stars are not centered on one another during the middle of an eclipse. This is because the plane that contains the orbits of the stars is tilted with respect to the observer. When the line of sight lies in the plane of the binary orbit, the orbital inclination is defined to be 90°. If the orbital inclination were zero, then the line of sight is perpendicular to the orbital plane of the binary system. Depending on the sizes of the stars, there is a critical value for the orbital inclination that will determine whether the stars eclipse one another or not.

II. Spectrophotometry

Instead of using a photographic emulsion to record a spectrum, astronomers often use a vidicon tube (similar to a TV camera) or CCD camera. These devices provide digitized spectral information. The digital information consists of pairs of numbers; one number is for brightness and the other for wavelength. Such information is readily stored in a computer and can be plotted to form what is called a spectrophotometric tracing or plot. The figure below is an example of such a spectrophotometric plot. The vertical axis indicates the relative brightness or **flux** and the horizontal axis displays the wavelength. In such a plot, absorption lines are indicated by the conical dips in brightness. Think of the spectral tracing as the profile of the spectrum's photograph (spectrogram).

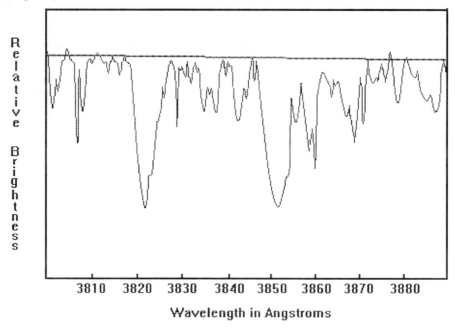

Figure 1. An example of a stellar spectrophotometric tracing

There are usually many absorption lines, some stronger than others. These spectral lines overlap one another and make the spectrum very complex. See Fig. 1 above. This complexity makes it uncertain as to exactly where the continuum level is. *The continuum level is the hypothetical brightness level that would be observed if there were no absorption lines.* This is indicated by the red horizontal line in Fig. 1. In this exercise, you are going to be asked to read the flux level of the continuum for several different spectrophotometric images or tracings.

III. The Data

Table I below lists the image numbers and corresponding orbital phases, at which each image was made, for 38 spectrophotometric images obtained by the IUE (International Ultraviolet Explorer) satellite telescope for the Y Cygni binary star system. The first six of these images are archival, having been obtained between 1979 and 1989 by various observers. The remaining 32 were obtained over one orbital cycle (2.9963 days) of the binary in May 1990 by R. H. Koch and R. J. Pfeiffer at NASA's Goddard Space Flight Center in Greenbelt, Maryland. This was the remote command center for controlling the telescope, which is in orbit around the center of the Earth at a distance of about 25,000 miles. Unfortunately, the spacecraft is no longer functioning, but it has provided us with an enormous amount of data over its lifetime and those data are still being analyzed.

You will analyze a certain spectral interval for 24 of these images in the form of spectrophotometric plots or graphs. Each plot comes from an image of the binary star's spectrum made at different times or phases during the orbital cycle of the system. Each of these separate plots has been made from a file containing two columns of data, the first is the wavelength in Angstroms and the second is absolute flux in units of ergs/cm^2/sec/Ångs. Each of these files constitutes a digitized portion of an image of the ultraviolet spectrum of the binary star. These images were made with the **S**hort **W**avelength **P**rimary vidicon camera of the spacecraft and are designated as SWP images.

Table I
IUE Images of Y Cygni with Keplerian Orbital Phases

SWP	Phase	SWP	Phase
06388	0.2156	38900	0.1237
10859	0.4060	38901	0.1363
19647	0.9301	38902	0.1496
19649	0.9650	38907	0.2741
24186	0.9952	38908	0.2909
26077	0.4329	38909	0.3053
38887	0.9427	38910	0.3192
38888	0.9567	38912	0.3526
38889	0.9705	38913	0.3671
38890	0.9843	38914	0.3842
38891	0.9981	38915	0.3992
38892	0.0123	38916	0.4125
38893	0.0257	38917	0.4279
38894	0.0411	38918	0.4433
38895	0.0550	38919	0.4564
38896	0.0681	38923	0.6135
38897	0.0834	38924	0.6269
38898	0.0971	38931	0.7098
38899	0.1104	38940	0.8133

IV. Plotting the Light Curve

EXCEL data files for the spectral images listed in Table 1 are available on-line at the bottom of the web page for this course under the link titled "Ex18.5 Spectral Images." Click on this title and a list of the spectral images will appear. Click on the first image to open the EXCEL file of data and then plot the data following the instructions given to you. Stretch the plot vertically to make it easier to read the mean flux level with 3 significant figure precision. You may have EXCEL add more horizontal lines to help you read the scale. Follow the instructions in the EXCEL tutorial to do this.

Examine the plots for each of the spectral images and determine the continuum flux level for the wavelength interval of each image. Then record a mean value for the flux level of the continuum for each image. Do this by taking a ruler and laying it horizontally through what you believe is the average flux level of the continuum between 1630Å and 1650Å, ignoring the strong absorption lines near 1640 Å. Refer to Fig. 1 above to see how this is done. It is better to take the reading high rather than low, but the important thing is to be consistent in the way you measure the continuum flux level from image to image, otherwise your light curve will be noisy. **There must always be 3 significant figures, even if they are zeros, E.G., 3.40 or 5.00.** Compile your results in the two-column table of phases and fluxes on the answer sheet.

Use the EXCEL tutorial instructions provided to enter the data you obtained for the continuum flux levels and the corresponding phases from Table 1 into EXCEL. Duplicate the data over the phase interval 0.00 to 0.10, add 1.00 to the values of the phases for these data points, and put these data at the end of the column. In this way, the light curve will repeat itself for a phase interval of 0.10 beyond phase 1.00 on the right side of your plot. See the example below:

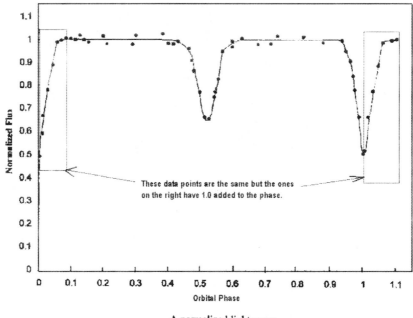

These data points are the same but the ones on the right have 1.0 added to the phase.

A normalized light curve

To facilitate analyzing the light curve, we need to normalize the flux values so that 1.00 is the average value of the flux outside the eclipses. To do this, use EXCEL to plot your data with phase along the x-axis and flux along the y-axis. Then examine the light curve and estimate the mean flux level outside the eclipses taking into account that your data may have larger errors. This mean value of the flux is the normalizing flux, referred to as NF in the EXCEL tutorial. So follow the instructions on how to divide all the flux values by this mean value and plot the results. Your graph should then look the example shown above.

After plotting your data, if you want to change the range of flux or phase along the axes, proceed as follows: Double click on the numbers along the x-axis and/or y-axis. This will open a menu for you to revise these numbers. When the graph is completed, save this as a file to your account on the network using the export function. Then print out your graph.

VI. Analyzing the Light Curve

Draw a smooth curve among the data points to show the changing flux of the system versus phase. Draw the curve in such a way that it takes into account the errors of the data and the eclipses are symmetrical about mid-eclipse, as shown in the example above. This is the theoretical light curve.

If secondary eclipse occurs at a phase other than 0.5, the orbit is not circular. Examine the light curve. At what phase does secondary conjunction occur? Record your answer; be very precise. Is the orbit circular or eccentric?

Determining the Light Ratio of the Stars:

If one eclipse is deeper than the other, then one star is brighter than the other. It is a geometric fact that the surface areas of the 2 stars that are eclipsed in both the primary eclipse and secondary eclipse are the same. So if one eclipse is deeper than the other, it is because one star has a greater surface brightness than the other.

When you determine the eclipse depths, make sure to allow for random noise in the measurements. The ratio of the eclipse depths is the light ratio of the stars. For example, if the eclipse depth at primary conjunction is 0.45 (distance from a flux level of 1.0 to a flux level of 0.55 at mid-eclipse) and 0.40 at secondary conjunction, then star 1 is brighter than star 2. The light ratio of the two stars (fainter to brighter) is then

$$\text{Light Ratio} = L_2/L_1 = 0.40 / 0.45 = 0.89. \tag{1}$$

(Recall that star 1 is the star eclipsed at phase 0.0, which is primary conjunction) This means that star 2 has 0.89 of the flux that star 1 has, that is, $L_2 = 0.89L_1$.

Determining the Light fractions of the Stars:

Now it must be that both normalized stellar fluxes add to 1.00. So, let f_1 be the normalized fractional flux of star 1 and f_2 the normalized fractional flux of star 2.

Then

$$f_1 + f_2 = 1.00 \tag{2}$$

Now the light ratio in equation (1) must be the same value as the normalized fraction flux ratio. That is:

$$L_2/L_1 = f_2/f_1$$

From the ratio of the eclipse depths, in the example above, f_2 then must be $0.89f_1$. Hence, $f_1 + .89 f_1 = 1.00$. Solving the latter equation for f_1 we get:

$$f_1 = 1.00/(0.89 +1) = 0.53$$

It then follows from equation (2) that $f_2 = 1.00 - 0.53$ or $f_2 = 0.47$.

It is not possible for both stars to have an eclipse depth greater than 0.50. Also, since the eclipses are not total, one works with eclipse depths rather than flux levels remaining during the eclipse. **Now determine f_2 and f_1 for the stars of Y Cyg and record your answers.** The values will be different than the ones given in the example above.

For Y Cyg, the inclination of the orbit to the line of sight of the observer is known to be 85.5 degrees. Hence, the eclipses are not as deep as they would be if the inclination were 90 degrees.

Determining the Stellar Radii:

From the theoretical light curve that you have drawn, you are going to determine the phase interval over which the eclipses occur. Make sure to allow for random noise in the measurements when you are determining the eclipse intervals and depths.

In the schematic to the right, the larger star is shown relative to the smaller star at 2 different orbital positions, assuming the orbital inclination to the line of sight is 90°. When the 2 stars are just touching one another, this is the beginning of an eclipse and is called 1st contact. In the second position the 2 stars are centered on one another. This is the middle of the eclipses and corresponds to the phases at which the light curve reaches a minimum, whether it be primary conjunction or secondary conjunction.

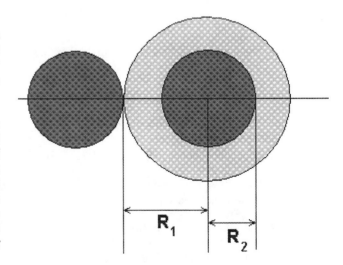

From your light curve determine the phase interval from 1st contact to the end of the entire eclipse for both the primary and secondary eclipses. This interval should be symmetrical about mid-eclipse for both eclipses. Divide each of these numbers in half to get the mean value for the phase interval from 1st contact to mid-eclipse. Record your answers for both eclipses. During these time intervals, the leading edge of the smaller star has moved a distance $R_1 + R_2$ relative to the larger star.

It is known that the speed of the smaller star relative to the larger star is 460 km per second.

How the orbital speeds of the stars are found is the matter in another exercise. Hence, you can compute the sum of the two stellar radii in km by multiply the speed times the number of seconds in the phase interval from 1st contact to the middle of the eclipse.

For example, suppose this phase interval is 0.0605. The actual value that you measure will be different.

The orbital period of Y Cygni is 2.9963 days.

So the number of days from 1st contact to the middle of the eclipse in our example is 0.0605 x 2.9963 days = 0.181days. **Record your answer for the phase interval in days on the answer page.**

How many seconds is this? It is: 0.181 days x 24 hours/day x 60 min/hr x 60 sec/min = 1.56 x 10^4 seconds. **Your answer will be somewhat different; record your answer for the phase interval in seconds.**

So then

$$R_1 + R_2 = \text{orbital speed x time} = 460 \text{ km/sec x } 1.5638 \times 10^4 \text{ secs.} = 7.19 \times 10^6 \text{ km.} \qquad (3)$$

Record the value that you get.

For the above, we have assumed there is no tilt of the orbital plane to the line of sight. However, this is not the case for Y Cygni, which is known to have an orbital inclination of 85.5°. Therefore, the above value for the sum of the stellar radii must now be divided by the sine of the orbital inclination to compensate for the tilt of the orbit to the line of sight. The sine of this angle is 0.997. Hence,

$$R_1 + R_2 = 7.19 \times 10^6 \text{ km / } 0.997 = D. \qquad (4)$$

Record the value that you calculate.

Now the Sun's radius is 6.96 x10^5 km. Therefore, **D** is 10.36 times larger than the Sun. Remember, your value for **D** will be different than the value given above.

If we knew the temperatures of the 2 stars we could find the ratio of the radii of the stars from the Stefan-Boltzmann Law. That is, the Luminosity of each star is L=$4\pi R^2 \sigma T^4$. If we divide the Luminosity of star 2 by the luminosity of star 1 we get:

$$L_2/L_1 = (R_2/R_1)^2 \, (T_2/T_1)^4, \qquad (5)$$

where $4\pi\sigma$ cancels out. Now we solve this equation for the ratio of the stellar radii. This first leads to:

$$(R_2/R_1)^2 = (L_2/L_1)(T_1/T_2)^4. \qquad (6)$$

Now we take the square root to get:

$$R_2/R_1 = (L_2/L_1)^{0.5}(T_1/T_2)^2. \qquad (7)$$

As a first approximation, the ratio of the luminosities is the same as the light ratio that you determined from the depth of the eclipses in equation (1). This is valid if the temperatures of the two stars are not too disparate. From our example above this light ration was 0.89. If we knew the temperatures of the stars we could now find the ratio of the stellar radii. Since we know the sum of the stellar radii from our calculation in equation (3) above and the ratio of the stellar radii from equation (7), we have 2 equations is 2 unknowns and we could find the individual sizes of the 2 stars.

The stellar temperature may be determined if we knew the spectral types of the 2 stars. But this is known from studying the spectral lines. The brighter star has spectral type **B0 IV** and the dimmer star is **B0.5 IV**. To find the temperatures of the stars we go on-line to **ads.harvard.edu/books, and then Zombeck's Handbook of Astrophysical Data, page 68.** You make take the values of the temperatures for luminosity class V instead of IV. **Record the values you find for the temperatures of the 2 stars.**

After you have the temperatures, you can compute the ratio of the stellar radii from (7) and then record this on the answer page.   Now we solve equation (7) algebraically for R_2 in terms of R_1 as follows:

$$R_2 = [(L_2/L_1)^{0.5}(T_1/T_2)^2]R_1. \tag{8}$$

Substitute this expression for R_2 into equation (4) for $R_1 + R_2$ and we get:

$$R_1 + [(L_2/L_1)^{0.5}(T_1/T_2)^2] R_1 = D. \tag{9}$$

Now factor R_1 from both terms on the left of (9) to get:

$$R_1 [1 + (L_2/L_1)^{0.5}(T_1/T_2)^2] = D.$$

Now solve the above equation for R_1 to get:

$$R_1 = D / [(L_2/L_1)^{0.5}(T_1/T_2)^2 + 1]. \tag{10}$$

We can simplify this by noting that the factor $(L_2/L_1)^{0.5}(T_1/T_2)^2$ is just R_2/R_1 from equation (7). Hence, we rewrite equation (10) as

$$R_1 = D / [R_2/R_1 + 1]. \tag{11}$$

So now calculate the value of R_1 from equation (11) and substitute this value of R_1 into equation (4) for $R_1 + R_2$ and solve for R_2.

Record the values you get for the stellar radii on the answer sheet.

This exercise demonstrates how astronomers are able to determine the sizes of stars by analyzing the light curves of eclipsing binary stars. In reality, we have greatly simplified the actual method that is used in analyzing light curves. For example, we have not explained how the orbital inclination and percentages of the surface areas of the stars that are eclipsed are determined.

Ex 18.5 Answer Page

PHASE	FLUX

PHASE	FLUX

1. Value of flux for normalizing the light curve: _____.

2. Phase of secondary conjunction or eclipse: _____.

3. Type of orbit: _____.

4. Depth of primary eclipse: _____ .   5. Depth of secondary eclipse : _____ .

6. Light ratio for the stars: _____ .

7. Light fractions f_1 = _____   8. Light fraction f_2 = _____ .

9. Phase interval from 1st contact to mid-eclipse for primary eclipse is _____ .

10. Phase interval from 1st contact to mid-eclipse for secondary eclipse is _____ .

11. Average value of the above phase interval is _____ .

12. Above phase interval in days is _____. This number of days in seconds is _____ .

13. Value of $R_1 + R_2$ = (orbital speed) x (time in seconds from above) is: _____ .

14. Value of $R_1 + R_2$ divided by sin i is _____ .

15. Temperatures of stars found on internet: T_1 = _____, and T_2 = _____ .

16. Value for R_2 / R_1 computed using temperature and light ratio is _____.

17. Value for R_1 = _____   18. Value for R_2 = _____ .

Exercise 18.7

The H-R Diagram and Spectroscopic Parallax

I. Introduction

Absolute magnitude is the brightness of an object when observed at a distance of 10 parsecs. Absolute magnitudes may be used to compare the intrinsic brightness of one star with another star, but only in a **relative way**. In this sense, the term *absolute magnitude* is a bit of a misnomer, because the absolute magnitude scale is a **relative** scale of intrinsic brightness. On the other hand, **luminosity** is an absolute measure of intrinsic brightness. That is, luminosity is expressed in actual units, such as watts, whereas absolute magnitudes are dimensionless numbers.

Absolute magnitudes can not be measured directly, they must be calculated after the apparent magnitude and parallax of the object are measured. The relationship among the absolute magnitude, M, apparent magnitude, m, and the distance of an object in parsecs, d, is:

$$M = m + 5 - 5 \log (d). \tag{1}$$

Table 1 lists the values of m, the spectral types, and parallaxes for several stars. Follow the instructions below for these stars:

1. Use the parallax to compute the distance of each star and record this in the table.
2. Then calculate the absolute magnitude of each star from equation (1) and tabulate this also.
3. Plot each of these stars in the schematic H-R Diagram given to you and label with the letter of the star or the star name. This H-R Diagram does not exactly agree with the one in the textbook, but don't worry about that.
4. From the position of the star in the H-R Diagram, identify the luminosity class and what type of star it is. For example: VII, white dwarf, or III, red giant. Record your answers in the table.

Table 2 lists stars with measured apparent magnitudes and known spectral types and luminosity classes.

5. Plot these stars on the H-R Diagram also, and label.
6. Read off their absolute magnitudes and record the value in the table.
7. Then calculate the distance of each star from equation (1) and record. This is the *spectroscopic parallax* method for finding distance.

Hand in the next page to your instructor when requested.

Exercise 18.7 Answer Sheet

Name _____ Lab Sec. _____ Date _____

Table 1

Star	Spec. Type	m	p(")	d(pc)	M	Lum. Class	Type of Star
A	B9	2.07	0.0340	_____	_____	_____	_____
B	F2	2.28	0.0520	_____	_____	_____	_____
C	K3	3.27	0.0320	_____	_____	_____	_____
D	G0	3.46	0.1720	_____	_____	_____	_____
α Per	F5	1.79	0.0050	_____	_____	_____	_____
λ Tau	B3	3.41	0.0080	_____	_____	_____	_____
δ Vir	M3	3.39	0.0163	_____	_____	_____	_____
α CMaB	O9	6.15	0.4070	_____	_____	_____	_____

Table 2

Star	Spec. Type	Lum. Class	m	M	d(pc)
G	M2	I	6.42	_____	_____
H	O9	V	7.55	_____	_____
J	A0	V	10.22	_____	_____
ε Cen	B1	III	2.29	_____	_____
KK	G5	II	8.56	_____	_____
λ Ori	O8	III	3.40	_____	_____
β Dor	F9	I	3.76	_____	_____

Schematic H – R Diagram

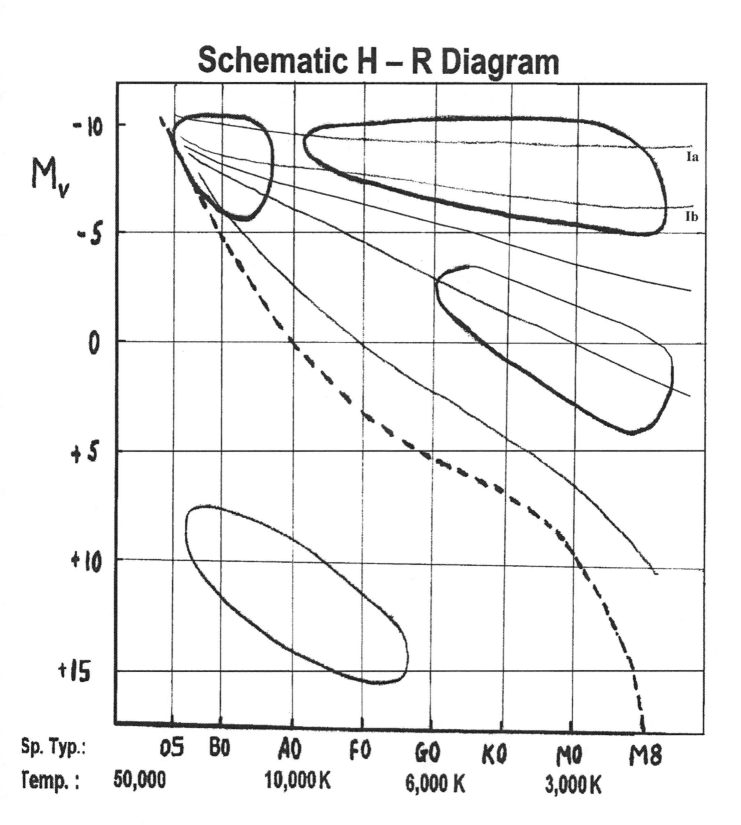

Ia

Ib

M_v

-10

-5

0

+5

+10

+15

Sp. Typ.: O5 B0 A0 F0 G0 K0 M0 M8

Temp. : 50,000 10,000 K 6,000 K 3,000 K

Exercise 19.0

SPECTROSCOPY

I. Introduction

Spectroscopy is the study of spectra. The light that we receive from the stars is a mixture of various colors or wavelengths. Much information about stars can be learned by spatially separating these different wavelengths to form a spectrum. The process of laterally separating the component wavelengths in a beam of light is called **dispersion**. Raindrops in the atmosphere disperse the sun's rays by acting like prisms to refract sunlight and form a rainbow. The colors are spatially separated because the amount of bending, or the angle of refraction, depends on wavelength. Therefore, a rainbow is an example of a spectrum produced by refractive dispersion.

Light can also be dispersed into a spectrum by reflection from, or transmission through, a surface that is ruled with many fine, closely spaced grooves. Such a device is called a diffraction grating. A phonograph record or CD is an example of a reflective diffraction grating. In this laboratory experiment, we shall employ a transmission grating. As light passes through the grating it is dispersed into a spectrum by thousands of fine, closely ruled grooves.

II. Types Of Spectra

There are three different kinds of spectra, depending on the physical conditions of the light source. This is summed up in what are called Kirchhoff's Laws of Spectroscopy:

First Law: An incandescent solid, liquid or gas under high pressure emits what is called a continuous spectrum.

That is, when the light from such sources is dispersed, the spectrum that is seen is a continuous band of wavelengths or colors. However, the spectrum is not uniformly bright. The brightness of the spectrum varies in a smooth way from short wavelengths (violet and blue) to long wavelengths (red). The color that is most intense is an indication of temperature. The way the colors vary in brightness, depending on temperature, is theoretically understood and summarized in what is called the Black Body Theory of Radiation.

> Question #1: What is the name of the equation that relates temperature to the wavelength of maximum brightness? You may have to refer to your text to answer this.

Second Law: A hot gas under low pressure produces an emission line spectrum.

In this case, we see only discrete wavelengths or colors called emission lines. Such a spectrum is also called a bright line spectrum. An example is shown below:

These wavelengths carry energies that match the energy differences between the electron states in the atoms of the particular gas that is being examined. If this same low pressure gas were cool and light consisting of all wavelengths were to pass through the gas, the atoms in the cool gas would absorb at exactly the same wavelengths it would emit when hot. Hence, we have the:

Third Law: **When a cool gas under low pressure intervenes between an observer and a source of a continuous spectrum, a dark line spectrum is seen.**

A dark line spectrum is essentially a continuous spectrum with noticeably reduced brightness at specific wavelengths. This is because the cool gas absorbed light at exactly the same wavelengths it emitted when it was hot. The spectrum we see when this happens is also called an **absorption** or **dark line spectrum**; these are synonymous terms. In 1814, Joseph Fraunhofer first cataloged such dark lines in the Sun's spectrum. For this reason, such a spectrum is also called a **Fraunhofer spectrum**.

In addition to the Sun, all stars show spectra that contain numerous absorption lines. Absorption lines are narrow bands of wavelengths in the spectrum where the light level is weak compared to the surrounding portion of the spectrum, which is called the **continuum**. This missing or weakened light has been absorbed by atoms in the relatively cooler layers of a star's atmosphere. Even though these layers are cooler than the much hotter photospheric layer of a star, the temperature in a stellar atmosphere is sufficiently high that all material there is in the gaseous form.

Now it is known from laboratory studies that the atoms of a given element, for example, hydrogen or calcium, absorb or emit light only at unique and specific wavelengths. As mentioned above, these wavelengths of light carry energies that characterize an element's atomic structure. More specifically, the energy carried by a given absorbed wavelength of light exactly matches the difference between two energy levels or states of an electron in the atom. The spectral lines for each element have been carefully measured and cataloged. Therefore, by comparing the wavelengths of the absorption lines seen in the spectrum of a star with those in a catalog, one can deduce qualitatively the chemical composition of the star's atmosphere. Think of the absorption lines to be like the fingerprints of the elements and that they can be used to identify which elements are present in a star's atmosphere. The problem is complicated by the fact that absorption lines of many elements are all mixed together in a star's spectrum.

III. Investigation Of Continuous Spectra

The device you shall employ to study spectra may be one of two types: (1) just a transmission grating that is mounted in a slide-type paper mount. The grating is very delicate and should be handled only by the paper mount. How a grating disperses the light is a complex matter and we shall not be concerned with the explanation. (2) a grating mounted in a black plastic device that is shaped like a piece of pie. This device has a slit at one end and a view port, holding the grating, opposite this. Inside there is a graduated wavelength scale upon which the spectrum may be seen projected. Either of these can be used to examine the spectra in the following.

We shall demonstrate some of the principles of the black body theory of radiation by studying the spectrum of an incandescent lamp. The lamp consists of a solid tungsten filament that will be heated by an electric current, much like the heating elements in a toaster. The temperature of the filament depends on the amount of electric current that flows through it. The amount of current can be varied by connecting the lamp to a rheostat, much like the dimmers that are used for some household lighting fixtures.

We start out with a low current and we note that the filament gives off a rather dim glow. Examine the source with your device.

2. What kind of spectrum do you see?
3. What color dominates the spectrum in brightness?
4. Slowly increase the voltage and observe the lamp directly with just your eye. What happens to the overall brightness and color of the filament as it gets hotter?
5. Turn the voltage regulator to its maximum value. The filament is now heated as high as it can be. What color dominates the spectrum in brightness?

6. What colors can be seen now, that were only barely visible or not visible at all when we were at the lowest temperature?
7. Examine the lamp directly with just your eye. What color does the filament appear to be?
8. What general rule do you conclude about the radiation that is emitted from an incandescent object as its temperature is increased (there are two things changing)?

IV. Investigation Of Emission Spectra

In this section, we investigate the emission spectra of several gases. We shall employ one of two possible techniques to measure the wavelengths you see in the spectra of certain samples and then try to identify what gas it is. The samples of gas are contained in long thin tubes that are called **discharge tubes.** The discharge tubes are plugged into a high voltage device that heats the gas and causes it to glow.

WARNING: UNPLUG THE POWER SUPPLY BEFORE ATTEMPTING TO INSERT OR REMOVE A TUBE. ALSO GRASP THE TUBE NEAR THE ENDS, NOT BY THE NARROW PART, OR YOU MAY BREAK THE TUBE OR GET A BAD BURN.

Again, you will use a transmission grating to disperse the light into a spectrum. If you are using device No. 1 described above, you will use the setup shown in Fig. 1 and calculate the wavelengths you see by measuring the positions of each emission line on a background scale. If you are using device No. 2, you need merely read the wavelengths of the emission lines you see projected onto the graduated scale inside the holder. In the later case, skip the next paragraph.

Instructions for Device 1:

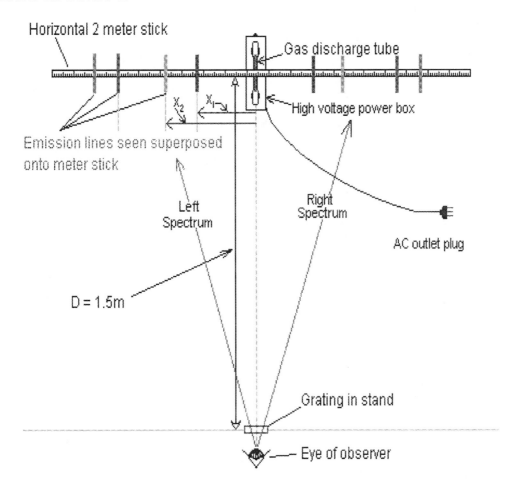

Exercise 19.0

Arrange your equipment to form the set-up shown in the above figure. The discharge tube should be placed at the center of the horizontal meter stick which will serve as the lateral background for the distance scale. The grating and discharge tube should be aligned along a line perpendicular to and at the center of the horizontal two-meter stick. After everything is properly set up and one looks through the grating at the discharge tube, one should see identical spectra formed to the left and right of the tube. The emission lines will be seen against the background of the meter stick and one objective will be to measure their distances, x, from the discharge tube. In addition, the distance from the horizontal meter stick to the grating must be measured very precisely. When this has been done for each line, its wavelength can be calculated from the following:

$$WL = 18950[\, x / (x^2 + D^2)^{1/2}\,],$$

where the wavelength, WL, is in Angstroms. The number 18950 accounts for the dispersive characteristics of the grating. D and x can be either in meters or centimeters. These values are to be recorded on the datasheet. Actually, you should make several measurements of x for each line and record the average value.

Record the wavelengths that you have determined, whether you used Device 1 or 2, for each gas sample on the answer sheet. Also record the color of each line and the identification code letter marked on the discharge tube. (If you used device 2, you will not have values for D or x, so leave these lines blank.) Then use the set of spectral line wavelengths that you have determined for each tube and the "Finding List of Spectral Lines" below to see if any of your samples can be identified.

There may not be enough tubes of the same gas for all teams. Therefore, it will be necessary to rotate the use of them in a cooperative way.

FINDING LIST OF SPECTRAL LINES

Argon	Helium	Hydrogen	Krypton	Mercury	Nitrogen	Neon	Xenon
4345.2	3888.7	3970.1 UV	4274.0	3984.0 violet	4099.9 violet	5400.6	4624.3
5151.4	4471.5	4101.7 violet	4319.6	4046.6 violet	4110.0	5852.5	4671.2
6043.2	4685.8	4340.5 indigo	4355.5	4358.5		6402.3	
6965.8	5015.7	4861.3 blue-green	4658.9	4797.0			
7067.2 deep red	5875.6	6562.9 red	4739.0	5460.7			
	6678.2		5570.3				
			5870.9				

Wavelengths given in Angstroms (10^{-8} cm)

SPECTROSCOPY ANSWER SHEET

I. Introduction

1. Temp.-wavelength equation:_____.

II. Investigation of Continuous Spectra

2. Type of spectrum:_____.

3. Brightest color:_____.

4. Change in brightness and color:_____

_____

_____.

5. Brightest color at max. temp: _____.

6. Colors previously not visible:_____.

7. Un-dispersed color:_____.

8. Generalized radiation rule for increasing temperature:_____

_____

_____.

III. Identification of Emission Line Sources

1. Source Code Letter:_____,   D=_____cm,   Element_____

    Line color_____, x=_____cm   WL=_____

    Line color_____, x=_____cm   WL=_____

    Line color_____, x=_____cm   WL=_____

    Line color_____, x=_____cm   WL=_____

2. Source Code Letter:_____,   D=_____cm,   Element _____

    Line color_____,   x=_____ cm   WL=_____

    Line color_____,   x=_____ cm   WL=_____

    Line color_____,   x=_____ cm   WL=_____

    Line color_____,   x=_____ cm   WL=_____

3. Source Code Letter : _____,   D=_____cm,   Element_____

    Line color_____,   x=_____ cm   WL=_____

    Line color_____,   x=_____ cm   WL=_____

    Line color_____,   x=_____ cm   WL=_____

    Line color_____,   x=_____ cm   WL=_____

4. Source Code Letter: _____,   D=_____cm,   Element_____

    Line color_____,   x=_____ cm   WL=_____

    Line color_____,   x=_____ cm   WL=_____

    Line color_____,   x=_____ cm   WL=_____

    Line color_____,   x=_____ cm   WL=_____

5. Source Code Letter:_____,   D=_____ cm,   Element_____

    Line color_____,   x=_____ cm   WL=_____

    Line color_____,   x=_____ cm   WL=_____

    Line color_____,   x=_____ cm   WL=_____

    Line color_____,   x=_____ cm   WL=_____

Exercise 20.0

DOPPLER SHIFTS AND RADIAL VELOCITIES

I. Introduction

In 1842, C. Doppler discovered that:

> **Any wave phenomenon, emitted by a source that is moving relative to an observer, is found to have wavelengths, λ, different than what would be observed if there were no relative motion.**

This is known as the **Doppler Effect**. It does not matter if the source is moving and the observer is at rest, the observer is moving and the source is at rest, or whether both are moving. Furthermore, only the component of the relative velocity or speed along a line connecting the observer and the source (the radial direction or line of sight) is significant and is called the **radial velocity.** Any component of the relative velocity that is perpendicular to the radial direction does not produce a Doppler effect. **The Doppler Effect applies to both light and sound waves.**

The wavelength observed or measured when there is relative motion is called λ_{meas}. The wavelength observed when there is no relative motion, that is, when the source is at rest with respect to the observer, is called the rest wavelength, λ_{rest}. The difference between these two wavelengths is called the **Doppler shift, $\Delta\lambda$**, which is defined by:

$$\Delta\lambda = \lambda_{meas} - \lambda_{rest}$$

The greater the relative motion or velocity, the greater the Doppler shift. Hence, the Doppler shift

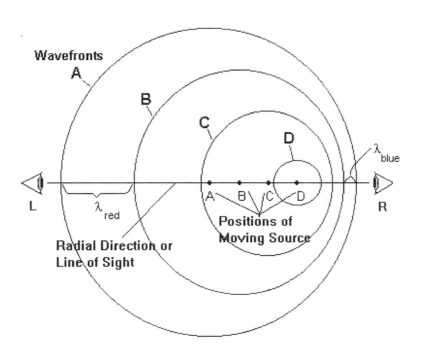

Figure 1. The Doppler Effect

161

is a direct indication of the relative speed of the source of the waves along an observer's line of sight to the source.

When we study the spectra of atoms in the laboratory, we assume that there is no relative motion of the source with respect to the observer. Hence, wavelengths measured in the laboratory are considered rest wavelengths. Therefore, rest wavelengths are also called laboratory wavelengths or λ_{lab}.

Let us discuss the Doppler effect in terms of the light or radiation we observe coming from stars. In Fig. 1, a star is moving along a line between two different observers labeled as L and R, for left and right. When the star was at position A, it emitted a wavefront, which has now expanded to the position shown as **A**. When the star was at position B it emitted a wavefront which has now expanded to position **B**. Similarly for C and D. The star's motion compresses the wavefronts in the direction the star is moving and stretches the distance between the wavefronts in the opposite direction. Hence, for the observer on the right, any spectral line will be measured to have a wavelength that is shorter than the wavelength measured in the laboratory for the atomic species producing that line. In this case, λ_{rest} is greater than λ_{meas} and the Doppler shift is a negative number. Since in the visible spectrum, the shorter wavelengths are blue ones, a negative Doppler shift is called a "blueshift". In astrophysical parlance, when an object is said to have a "blueshift", it means that that object is moving towards the Earth or the Sun.

On the other hand, if a star is moving away or receding from us, as for the observer on the left in the diagram, a specific wavelength of radiation will be measured to have a longer wavelength than that measured in the laboratory. In this case, the Doppler shift will be a positive number and it is said that the Doppler shift is a "redshift." Hence, when astronomers say a star, planet, or galaxy has a redshift, it means that object is moving away from us. Furthermore, the speed of recession or approach is proportional to the amount of the Doppler shift.

Examine the diagram below (Fig. 2) which shows schematic spectra for three different cases of relative motion. The top spectrum shows the spectrum of a star that is approaching us and, therefore, the various spectral lines are blueshifted. The middle spectrum is an emission spectrum emitted by a mixture of gases producing the same spectral lines in the laboratory. The spectral lines in this spectrum have wavelengths that are considered to be rest wavelengths. The values of these rest wavelengths in Angstroms (Å) are written at the top of the diagram The bottom spectrum is one for a star that is receding from us. Its spectral lines are redshifted with respect to the laboratory wavelengths. In the diagram, the Doppler shifts are exaggerated for clarity.

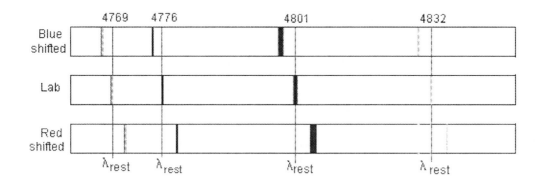

Figure 2. Schematic spectra illustrating Doppler Shifts for 3 different cases.

II. Calculating Radial Velocity

Now consider the 4801A line in the top spectrum of Fig. 2. The Doppler shift for this spectral line has been measured to be: $\Delta\lambda$ = -2.9 Å. The minus sign indicates that the Doppler shift is a

Exercise 20.0

blueshift. The relative speed of this star along the line of sight, which is called the radial velocity, **v**, can be calculated using Doppler's equation:

$$\mathbf{v} = (\Delta\lambda \, / \, \lambda_{rest}) \; \mathbf{c}$$

In this equation $c = 3\times10^5$ km/sec, the speed of light. Doing the calculation we obtain that **v** for this star is -181 km/sec. You should verify this calculation. The value of 181 km/sec is rather large for stellar speeds relative to the sun in this part of the galaxy, but it is only meant to illustrate the method of determining radial velocity from a Doppler shift.

III. Spectrophotometry

Figure 2 is a schematic diagram of the way spectra appear in a spectrogram, that is, in a photograph of a spectrum. Instead of using a photographic emulsion to record a spectrum, astronomers often use a vidicon tube or CCD camera. These devices provide digitized spectral information. The digital information consists of pairs of numbers, one number is for brightness and the other for wavelength. Such information is readily stored in a computer and can be plotted to form what is called a spectrophotometric tracing. Figure 3 is an example of such a spectrophotometric tracing. The vertical axis indicates the relative brightness or **flux** and the horizontal axis displays the wavelength in Angstroms. In such a plot, absorption lines are indicated by the conical dips in brightness. Think of the spectral tracing as the profile of the spectrum's photograph.

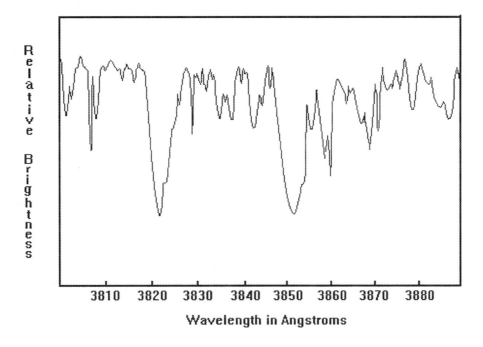

Figure 3. An example of a stellar spectrophotometric tracing

Fig 3. is more realistic in terms of what a stellar spectrum may look like. That is, there are many more lines shown, some stronger than others. Spectral lines overlap one another and make it uncertain as to exactly where the continuum level is. However, once a line can be identified in the sense that we know which atom produced the line and what its laboratory wavelength is, we can determine the measured wavelength using the wavelength scale. Once this is done, it is possible to compute the Doppler shift for the star.

Fig. 3 and the other images on the following pages are spectrophotometric tracings for a binary star called PB1 Ori. Each tracing is an image of the binary star's spectrum made at different times during the orbital cycle of the system. The photometric orbital phase is given at the top of each image. Since there are two stars of nearly the same brightness in the system, every spectral line is doubled. This makes things a bit more complicated but tractable for measuring separate Doppler shifts for each star. This is because each spectral line of one star is separated from the corresponding spectral line of the other star by the Doppler shifts that result from the different orbital velocities of the two stars. That is, most of the time one star is approaching us while the other is receding. This is because the orbital plane is tilted in space in such a way that it nearly contains the line of sight towards the system.

When the stars are near conjunction (photometric phases 0.0 and 0.5), they are moving nearly perpendicular to the line of sight and the Doppler separation of the separate lines for each star is very small. The image for phase 0.030 is such an image. Notice how the strong spectral feature near 3852.3 Å appears to be almost one line. Furthermore, at this phase, one star may be partially eclipsing the other, thereby making the eclipsed star's line weaker.

On the image for phase 0.081 (below) one can see that there are two distinct lines, one for each star, separated by several Angstroms.

IV. THE RADIAL VELOCITY CURVE

Use the following images to determine the radial velocity curve and mass ratio for the binary star PB1, after determining the chart scale for the spectral images.

1. On each image, locate the center of each of the two components of the line near 3853 Å. Remember that a given spectral line will have a separate component for each star except for the phases near conjunction, when each star's line is blended with the other star's line. Measure the distances of the centers of the lines in cm for Star 1 from the left edge of the chart (which is at 3800Å) and record these values on the answer sheet as **Dcm.**
2. Use the chart scale to convert the values of **Dcm** to Angstroms and record this value as **DAng.**
3. Add these values to 3800Å and we now have the **measured** values for the wavelength for the spectral line of Star 1. Record this as λ_{meas}. Remember, this is the measured wavelength for use in Doppler's equation.
4. Repeat for the other star. You will need to print out two answer sheets to record all the data.

As you go from one phase to another, be sure to keep track of which star has the blueshift and which has the redshift. **Which star has the larger velocity, algebraically, will reverse at the stellar conjunctions (phase 0.50).**

6. Now compute the Doppler shifts for each star for each image using your measured wavelengths and the lab or **rest wavelength of 3852.31 Å**. Record these values as $\Delta\lambda$.
7. Next, use Doppler's equation to compute the corresponding radial velocities for the stars. Record these as **RV1** and **RV2.**
8. Now plot the radial velocities for each star versus orbital phase on the same piece of graph paper, using Excel. An example of such a radial velocity diagram is shown below. Make sure the horizontal scale is for orbital phase.
9. Once step 8 has been accomplished, draw a separate **smooth** curve among the data points for each star, allowing for the fact that your data points have errors. **Do not merely connect your data points with a curve or straight lines.**

Exercise 20.0

Also, condition your two curves to be drawn in such a way that **the two places where the two radial velocity curves intersect are at the same velocity.** The later points are not necessarily for zero velocity and indicate the radial velocity of the center of mass of the binary system relative to the Sun. Furthermore, the places on the curves where each star has a maximum radial velocity, either positive or negative, must be at the same phase.

10. Once you have drawn your radial velocity curves, it should be possible to read off the value for the radial velocity for the center of mass of the binary. This is called **the gamma velocity** of the binary. Record your result on the answer sheet.

Your radial velocity diagram should look similar to the one below, where radial velocity in km/sec is plotted along the vertical scale and orbital phase is plotted along the horizontal scale. CMV indicates the value of the radial velocity for the center of mass of the binary star. Notice how smooth continuous radial velocity curves are drawn for each star among the paired sets of data points. Your errors will probably be larger than those shown in the diagram.

The ratio of the absolute values of any pair of velocities, **measured relative to the center of mass**, at any phase is the **mass ratio** of the two stars. Such a pair of velocities is indicated in the diagram below. The mass ratio is a number that can never be greater than 1.00, that is, it is the smaller velocity divided by the larger velocity.

11. Now find the corresponding maximum radial velocities of each star in PB1 at the phases 0.25 and 0.75. **These values are to be read from the curves that you have drawn, relative to the gamma-velocity.** Record these values on the answer sheet. The stars should have radial velocities of opposite signs at the same phase.
12. Compute the ratios of the absolute values of the maximum radial velocities of the stars found at phases 0.25 and 0.75 and record on the answer sheet. Are they the same?

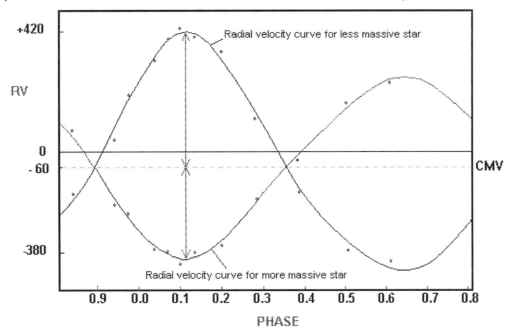

The above figure is a hypothetical radial velocity diagram for a binary star system with an elliptical orbit and stars that are different in mass. The phases are spectroscopic ones not photometric phases, so maximum velocities do not occur at phases 0.25 and 0.75.

DOPPLER SHIFTS AND RADIAL VELOCITIES
ANSWER AND WORK SHEET

Measured distance for wavelength range on charts: _____ (cm).

Chart scale for spectral images on charts: _____ Å/cm.

Star 1 Data   **Star 2 Data**

Phase	D_{cm}	D_{Ang}	λ_{meas}	$\Delta\lambda$	RV1	D_{cm}	D_{Ang}	λ_{meas}	$\Delta\lambda$	RV2

Gamma Velocity for PB1: _____ km/sec

Value of RV for star 1 at phase 0.25 read from Radial Velocity Curve: _____

Value of RV for star 2 at phase 0.25 read from Radial Velocity Curve: _____

Absolute Value of ratio of smaller RV to larger RV at phase 0.25 (**Mass Ratio**):   _____

Value of RV for star 1 at phase 0.75 read from Radial Velocity Curve: _____

Value of RV for star 2 at phase 0.75 read from Radial Velocity Curve: _____

Absolute value of ratio of smaller RV to larger RV at phase 0.75 (**Mass Ratio**):   _____

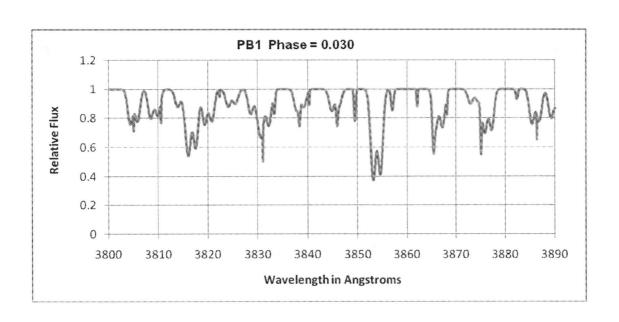

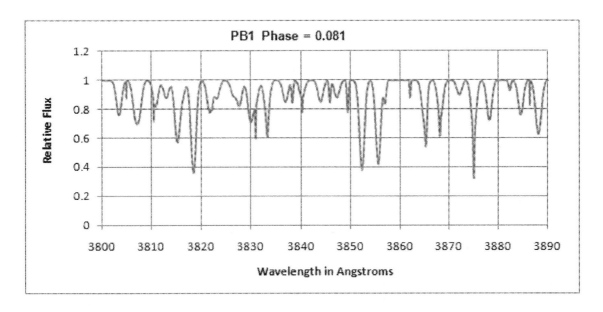

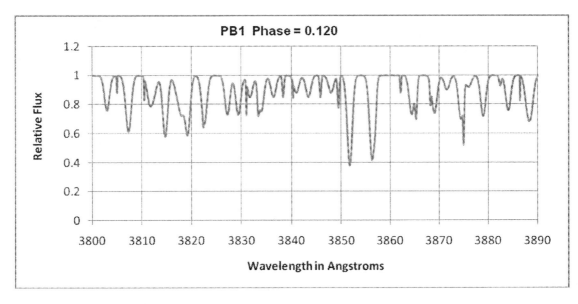

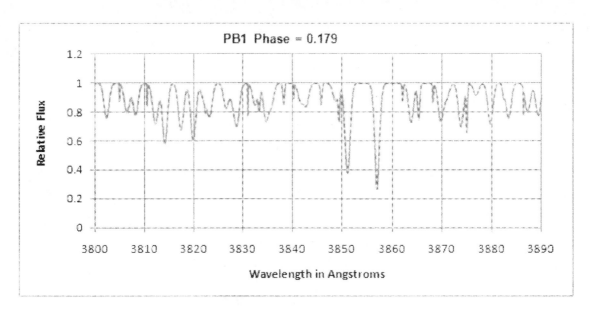

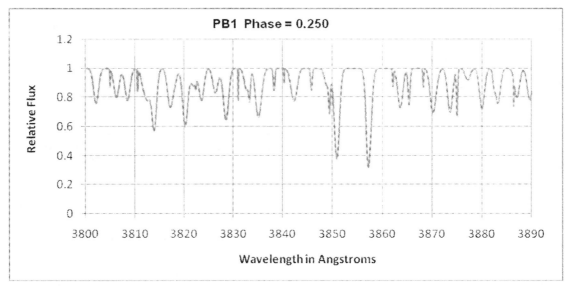

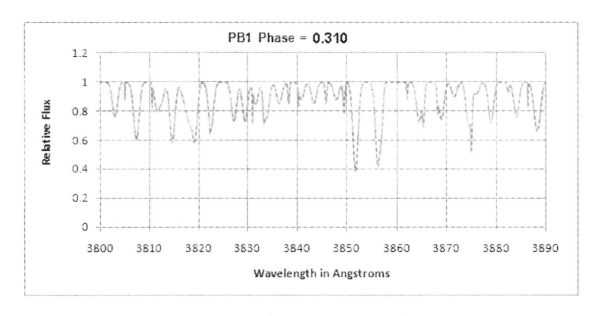

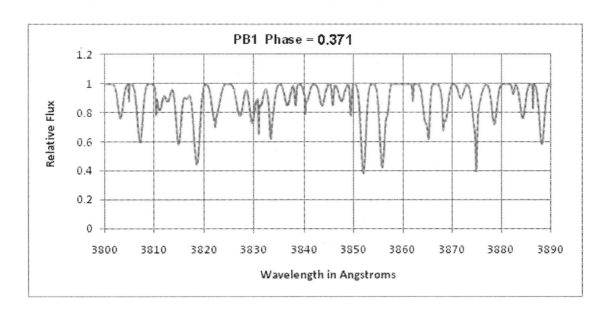

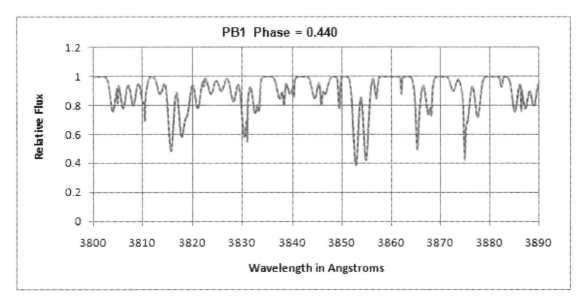

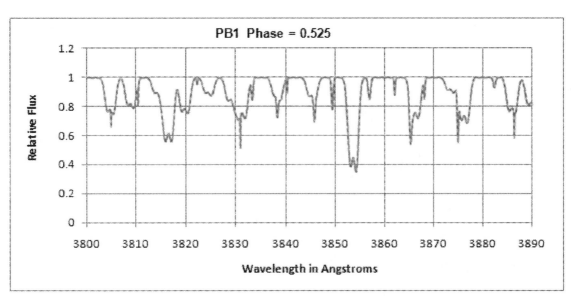

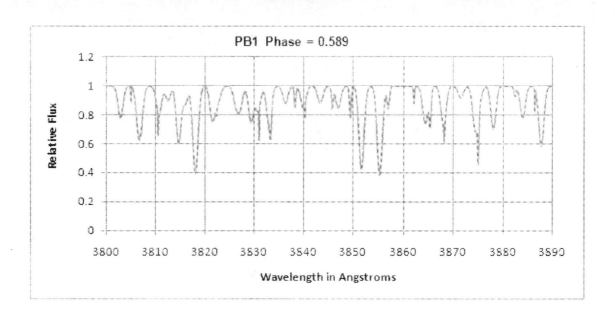

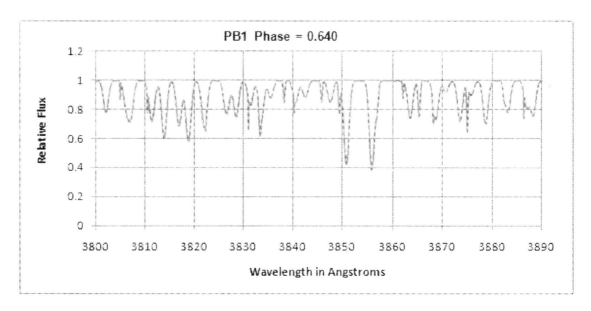

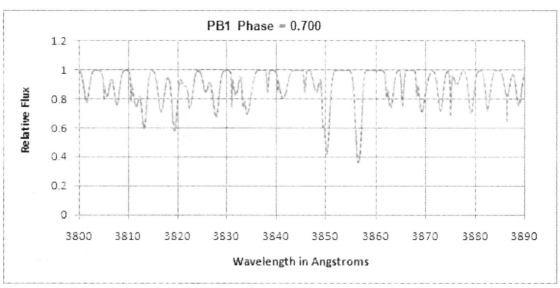

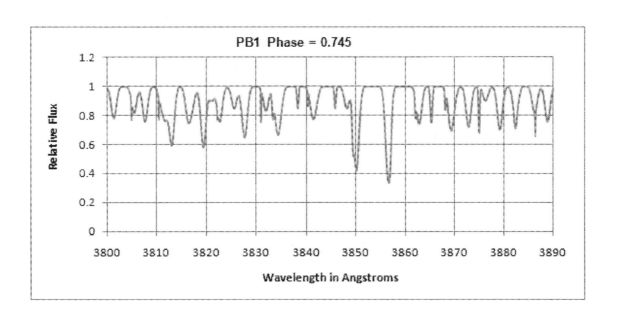

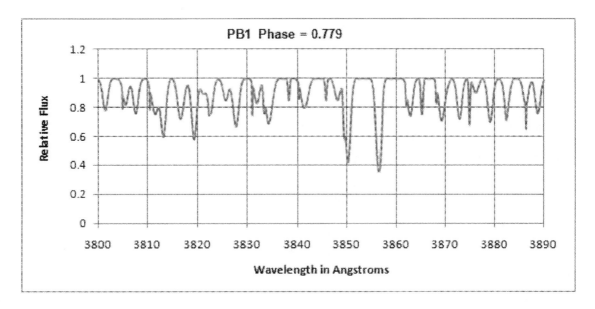

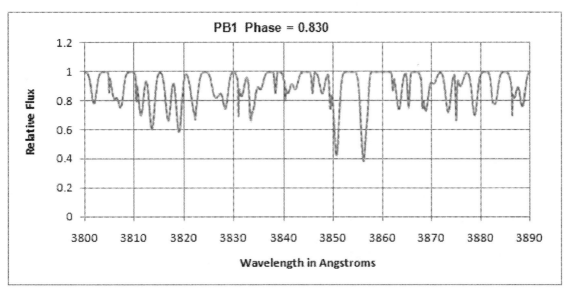

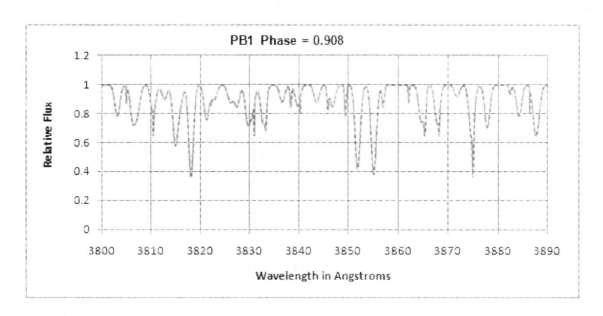

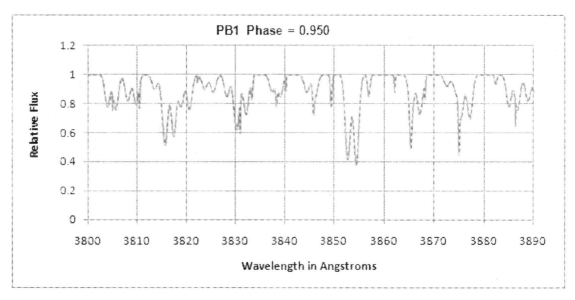

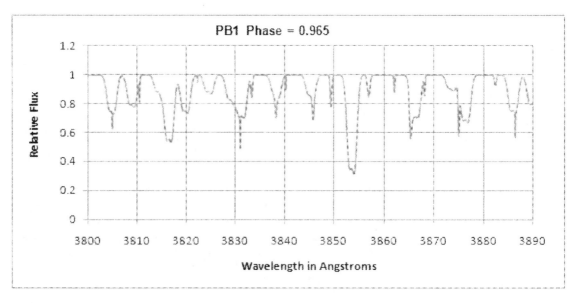

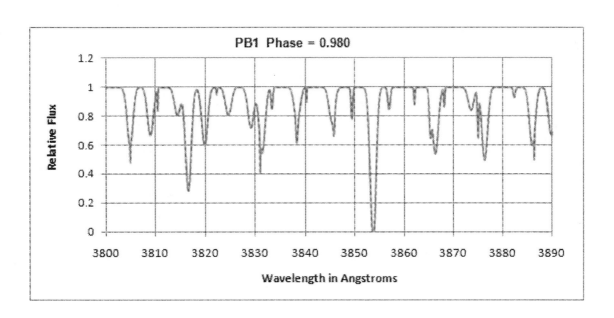

APPENDIX A

GLOSSARY

Almucantar: A circle connecting all points with the same altitude; a circle lying in a plane parallel to the plane of the celestial horizon.

Altitude (Alt): The angular distance of an object from the celestial or astronomical horizon. Negative altitudes indicate an object is below an observer's horizon and not visible.

Analemma: A curve that closely approximates the shape of a figure 8 meant to represent the value of the "equation of time" at different times of the year.

Arcmeasure: A numerical system used for expressing distances along an arc or curve using units, such as degrees, that are a fraction of a circle.

Arcminute: One sixtieth of a degree.

Arcsecond: One sixtieth of an arcminute.

Aspect: Synonymous with configuration.

Autumnal equinox (AE): The point on the celestial sphere where the Sun crosses the celestial equator as it appears to move from north to south of the equator.

Azimuth (Azi): The angular distance measured eastward along the celestial horizon from the north point to the vertical circle passing through a celestial object. Azimuth ranges from 0° through 360° at the north point of the horizon.

Celestial equator (CE): The great circle on the celestial sphere that is everywhere 90° from either celestial pole.

Celestial or Astronomical horizon (CH): The great circle on the celestial sphere that is everywhere 90° from the zenith and nadir.

Circumpolar Stars: Stars that have their diurnal circles either entirely above (perpetual apparition) or entirely below (perpetual occultation) the celestial horizon for an observer.

Configuration: A term referring to a specific elongation for a planet, such as, conjunction or opposition.

Conjunction: The aspect or configuration of a planet when its elongation is 0°.

Declination (Dec, δ): The angular distance of a celestial object north (+) or south (-) of the celestial equator.

Diurnal Circle (DC): the apparent path an object makes around the celestial sphere or around an observer as a result of the Earth's rotation. They are parallels of declination.

Diurnal motion or rotation: An apparent motion seen in the sky as a result of the Earth's rotation.

Equinoctial Colure (EC): the great circle on the celestial sphere that passes through the celestial poles and the equinoxes. One half the EC is the hour circle for RA $0^{h} 00^{m}$ and the other half is for RA $12^{h} 00^{m}$.

Ecliptic: The apparent path of the Sun around the celestial sphere as a result of the Earth's revolution; the projection of the Earth's orbit onto the celestial sphere.

Ecliptic Poles: The two points on the celestial sphere connected by a line perpendicular to the plane of the Earth's orbit.

Elongation: the angular distance of an object eastward or westward from the Sun as measured along the ecliptic.

Equation of Time (ET): the numerical difference between local apparent solar time and local mean time.

Gamma velocity: The velocity of the barycenter of a system, such as a binary star, relative to the Sun.

Greatest Elongation: The angle between a line of sight to the Sun and a line of sight that is tangent to the orbit of an inferior planet. See Exercise 15.0.

Hour angle (HA): The angular distance of a celestial object east or west from the local celestial meridian. Eastern hour angles are negative for computational purposes.

Hour circle (HC): The half of a great circle on the celestial sphere that extends from one celestial pole to the other; a semicircle connecting all points with the same RA and the same hour angle.

Inferior Planets: Planets that have orbits smaller in radius than the Earth's orbit around the sun.

Local apparent solar time (LAT): The hour angle of the real Sun plus 12:00.

Local Celestial Meridian (LCM): The great circle on celestial sphere connecting the south point of the horizon, the zenith, the celestial poles, the north point of the horizon, and the nadir.

Local Mean Time (LMT): The hour angle of the mean sun plus 12:00.

Lunar orbital node (LON): The points of intersection of the Moon's orbit and the ecliptic. Also see nodes.

Local Sidereal Time (LST): The western hour angle of the vernal equinox; the RA of any object making upper transit; the time elapsed, at the sidereal rate, since the last upper transit of the vernal equinox.

Lower Transit (LT): The event when an object crosses the LCM with its minimum altitude, the hour angle of that object then being 12 hours.

Nadir: The point in the sky directly below an observer and 180° from the zenith.

North ecliptic pole (NEP): See ecliptic poles.

North celestial pole (NCP): One of two points where the axis of rotation of the Earth pierces the celestial sphere.

Nodes: The two points of intersection between two orbits, such as, the Earth's orbit around the sun and the Moon's orbit around the Earth.

North Point of the Horizon (NPH): The point on the horizon that is the direction of true north for an observer; the point on the horizon from which azimuth is measured; a point of intersection of an observer's LCM and the celestial horizon.

Opposition: The aspect or configuration of a planet when its elongation is 180°.

Parallax: Half the apparent angular displacement suffered by a relatively nearby object, relative to much more distance objects, when viewed from two different positions.

Prime Vertical: The great circle on the celestial sphere passing through the east point of the horizon, the zenith, and the west point of the horizon.

Quadrature: The aspect or configuration of a planet when its elongation is 90° E or W.

Regression: Going backwards. In the sky or on the celestial sphere, westward is backwards while eastward is considered the prograde direction. The equinoxes and the lunar orbital nodes regress.

Right Ascension (RA, α): The angular distance (expressed in time units) of an object measured eastward from the vernal equinox.

Sexagesimal: A numerical system based on the number sixty.

South Celestial Pole (SCP): One of two points where the axis of rotation of the Earth pierces the celestial sphere.

South Point of the Horizon (SPH): The point on the horizon that is the direction of true south for an observer; the point on the horizon where the azimuth is 180°; a point of intersection of an observer's LCM and the celestial horizon.

Summer Solstice (SS): The point on the ecliptic where the Sun is at its greatest angular distance (declination) north of the celestial equator.

Superior Planets: Planets that have orbits larger than the Earth's orbit around the Sun.

Upper Transit (UT): The event when an object crosses the LCM at maximum altitude, the hour angle then being 0 hours.

Vernal Equinox (VE): The point on the ecliptic where the Sun crosses the celestial equator as it appears to move from south to north.

Vertical Circle: A semicircle on the celestial sphere that extends from the zenith to the nadir and connects all points with the same azimuth.

Winter Solstice (WS): The point on the ecliptic where the sun is at its greatest angular distance (declination) south of the celestial equator.

Zenith (Z): The point on the celestial sphere directly overhead or 90° from every point on the celestial horizon.

Zenith distance (ZD): The angular distance of a celestial object from the zenith.

Zodiac: A band of twelve constellations, girdling the celestial sphere, and centered on the ecliptic.

Zone Time (ZT): The local mean time of the central meridian of a time zone, e.g., the LMT of the 75th meridian for the Eastern Time Zone.

APPENDIX B

FINDING LIST OF CELESTIAL OBJECTS

1. Autumn Evening Sky

RA	Dec.	Type	Name/Remarks
21: 30	+12:10	Glob. Clus.	M15, in Pegasus
21: 34	-00:50	Glob. Clus.	M2; in Aquarius
22: 28	+58:10	Dbl Star	δ Cep; Sep=41"; mags=3.9 & 7.5; brighter star pulsates
00: 43	+41:16	Spiral. Gal.	M31; in Andromeda
01: 34	+30:39	Spiral Gal.	M33; in Triangulum
02: 08	+42:06	Dbl Star	γ And; Sep=10"; mags=3.0 & 5.0; blue and gold
02: 19	+57:10	Open Clus.	h Persei
02: 22	+57:07	Open Clus.	χ Persei
03: 47	+24:10	Open Clus.	M45, Pleaides; in Taurus

2. Winter Evening Sky

RA	Dec.	Type	Name/Remarks
05: 29	-02:20	Dbl Star	d Ori; Sep=53"; mags=2.0 & 6.8
05: 35	+22:01	Nebula	M1, Crab Nebula, Supernova remnant, in Taurus
05: 36	-02:36	Mltpl Star	σ Ori; mags=4.0, 7.0, 7.5 & 10.0 plus other faint stars
05: 36	-05:22	Nebula	M42, contains Trapeziu, in Orion
05: 52	+32:33	Open Clus.	M37; in Auriga
06: 47	-20:44	Open Clus.	M41; in Canis Majoris
08: 40	+20:02	Open Clus.	M44; Praesepe or Beehive, in Cancer
08: 44	+28:57	Dbl Star	ι Can; Sep=31"; mags=4.4 & 6.5

3. Spring Evening Sky

RA	Dec.	Type	Name/Remarks
09: 55	+69:04	Spiral Gal.	M81; in Ursa Major
13: 22	+55:11	Binary Star	Mizar; ζ UMa; Sep=15"; mags=2.1 & 4.2; Alcor nearby
13: 30	+47:12	Spiral Gal.	M51, Whirlpool Galaxy, in Canes Venatici
13: 42	+28:22	Glob. Clus.	M3, in Canes Venatici
14: 14	+51:36	Dbl Star	i Boo; Sep=38"; mags=4.9 & 7.5
15: 20	+02:06	Glob. Clus.	M5, in Serpens
16: 06	+17:12	Dbl Star	κ Her; Sep=30"; mags=5.0 & 6.0
16: 09	-19:21	Dbl Star	v Sco; Sep=41"; mags=4.2 & 6.5
16: 42	+36:28	Glob. Clus.	M13, in Hercules

4. Summer Evening Sky

RA	Dec.	Type	Name/Remarks
17: 31	+55:14	Dbl Star	v Dra; Sep=62"; mags=4.6 & 4.6
18: 02	-23:02	Nebula	M20, Trifid Nebula, in Sagittarius
18: 03	-24:23	Nebula	M8, Lagoon Nebula, in Sagittarius
18: 22	-16:11	Nebula	M17, Horseshoe Nebula, in Sagittarius
18: 36	-23:55	Glob. Clus.	M22, in Sagittarius
18: 43	+34:35	Dbl Star	ε Lyr; Sep=208"; mags=4.6 & 4.9; each is a binary
18: 51	-06:16	Open Clus.	M11, in Scutum
18: 54	+33:03	Plan. Neb.	M57, Ring Nebula, in Lyra
19: 29	+27:51	Dbl Star	β Cyg; Sep=35"; mags=3.0 & 5.3; TCNJ star (blue & gold)
19: 56	+22:43	Plan. Neb.	M27, Dumb-bell Nebula, in Vulpecula
21: 07	+38:45	Dbl Star	32 Cyg; Sep=30", mags=5.2 & 6.0

APPENDIX C

CONVERSIONAL PROCEDURES

This appendix illustrates several procedural methods for converting a number from one system to another.

1. Converting centimeters to time units using a chart scale.

For example, find the number of hours corresponding to a measured distance of 5.76 cm on a chart that has a right ascension chart scale of 1.205 hr/cm.

Step 1. Multiply the number of centimeters by the chart scale.

$$5.76 \text{ cm} \times 1.205 \text{ hr/cm} = 6.94 \text{ hr.}$$

The answer has been rounded off to 3 significant figures, the precision of the least precise number of those being multiplied.

Step 2. If it is desired to convert 6.94 hr to sexagesimal form, proceed as in 2, below. The answer is $6^h 56^m$ or 6:56, to the nearest whole minute.

2. Converting decimal hours to sexagesimal hours and minutes

For example, convert 8.53 hours to sexagesimal hours and minutes:

Step 1. Take the decimal part of the hours and multiply this by 60 minutes per hour:
$$0.53 \text{ hr} \times 60 \text{min/hr} = 31.8 \text{ min.}$$
Step 2. Round the decimal part of the number of minutes to the nearest whole minute.
$$31.8 \text{ min} = 32 \text{ min}$$
Step 3. Now write the result in sexagesimal form, e.g., hh:mm, where hh is the number of hours and mm is the number of minutes.

So 8.53 hr = 08:32 or $8^h 32^m$.

3. Converting sexagesimal time to decimal time

For example, convert 8:32, or $8^h 32^m$ to decimal hours:

Step 1. Divide the number of minutes by 60 hr/min:

$$32 \text{ min} /60 \text{ min/hr} = 0.53 \text{ hr.}$$

Step 2. Add the above to the whole number of hours:

$$8.00 \text{ hr} + 0.53 \text{ hr} = 8.53 \text{ hr.}$$

4. Converting arcmeasure to an equivalent amount of time for the Earth's rotation.

For example, convert 55.84 degrees to hours and minutes. This is really finding the amount of time it will take the Earth to rotate through this angle.

Step 1. Divide the angle by the angular rate of rotation of the Earth, which is 15.00 deg/hr:

$$55.84 \text{ deg} / 15.00 \text{ deg/hr} = 3.723 \text{ hr.}$$

Step 2. If it is desired to express 3.723 hr. in sexagesimal form, proceed as in method 2, above. To the nearest whole minute, the answer is $3^h 43^m$

5. Convert a time interval into arcmeasure.

For example, convert $3^h 43^m$ into degrees.

Step 1. Use procedure 3 to convert sexagesimal time to decimal time. The answer is 3.72 hr.
Step 2. Multiply the number of decimal hours by the angular rate of rotation of the Earth:

$$3.72 \text{ hr} \times 15.00 \text{ deg/hr} = 55.80 \text{ deg.}$$

Step 3. If it is desired to convert this to sexagesimal arcmeasure, multiply the number of decimal degrees by 60 arcmin/degree:

$$0.80 \text{ deg} \times 60 \text{ arcmin/deg} = 48.0 \text{ arcmin.}$$

Step 4. Write the result in sexagesimal form: $55^0 48'$.

APPENDIX D
Obtaining Hardcopy of the Monitor Screen Image

1. Make sure a green camera icon for the software, *Snagit*, is on the bottom menu bar. If not, click on the *Snagit* icon on the main area of the screen. When the *Snagit* window opens, minimize it.

2. Run *Skylab* and obtain the chart that you want to print.

3. Press ALT & ENTER (a new, smaller window will open with your chart)

4. Press the PRINT SCREEN key (upper right on keyboard). Another window will open. Click to maximize this window in the usual way.

5. Set the mouse cursor (now a cross-hair) in the uppermost left corner of the white menu bar (not in the blue menu bar with the "**Dos Box**"), click, and then drag down to the right bottom to encapsulate the entire chart. To be sure that you have encapsulated the entire chart, you may drag down past the chart into the white area.

6. Now move the mouse cursor to the menu bar above the encapsulated image and click on "crop." The snagit window will now show what is to be printed.

7. Now click "Image" on the top menu bar,
    > Then click on "Scale,"
    >> Click on "200%." This will make the chart fill the page. Do not print a chart that is not the size of an entire page.

8. Click "Colors" on menu bar
    > Click on "Invert." This reverses white and black colors. Do not print out a chart with a black background; it will be useless and a waste of ink.

9. Click on "File," then
    > Page setup, then
    >> Properties,
    >>> Then click on the "Basics" tab."
    >>> Then click on landscape,
    >>>> Then click OK, and you return to the previous window.
    >>>> Click OK again in this window.
    It may only be necessary to do step 9 the first time when getting a hard copy.

10. Click on the menu bar button with the green check mark where it says "Finish." This sends the image to the printer.

11. Click on the light blue bar at the top of the window with your chart image where it says "DOSBOX." The bar will change to dark blue indicating the window is activated.

12. Press ALT & ENTER and the *Skylab* screen returns. If *Skylab* does not immediately return, you may have to do this twice.